The early reviews are u~~~~~~~~~
in Washington is a laugh~~~~~~~~~~~~~~~~~~~~~~~~~~~~~~~

A hilarious take on lobbying and Congress today.
—WKZO

Snappy book on how stuff gets done in Washington . . .
I forgot it was fiction. It sometimes reads like the actual
nonsense that has happened in DC.
—Netgalley reviewer

Exactly the kind of comic relief I needed.
—Goodreads reviewer

ALSO BY GEORGE FRANKLIN

Incentives
The Holy Water of Free Enterprise

George Franklin takes a humorous look at the world of economic development with politicians, corporations, and a cast of rogue characters all wallowing in the government trough in the name of capitalism and free enterprise. *Incentives* is an uproarious, entertaining story of the hypocrisy that permeates public policy today.

So You Think You Want to Run for Congress
The True Grit of the Political Campaign

A firsthand account of what motivates someone to run for political office and the demands of mounting a major congressional campaign. Fundraising, personal attacks, petty politics and the absurdity of a political undertaking are all detailed in this humorous and informative narrative on the state of elections today. A must-read for anyone contemplating a run for elective office at any level.

Raisin Bran and Other Cereal Wars
30 Years of Lobbying for the Most Famous Tiger in the World

Powerful corporate interests use their lobbyists to wield influence. They impact our daily lives, but who are they and how do they operate? In this tell-it-like-it-is casual narrative, the reader gets an inside look at the life of a corporate lobbyist from someone who lived it. The book takes you from fundraisers, to the halls of Congress, to the White House and on to China, South Africa, and Mexico with a stop at Ground Zero just days after 9/11.

A Feeding Frenzy in Washington

GEORGE FRANKLIN

A NOVEL

A FEEDING FRENZY
IN WASHINGTON

FPA BOOKS

A Feeding Frenzy in Washington
© 2023 George Franklin

This book is a work of fiction. Names, characters, places, and incidents are either products of the author's imagination or used factiously. Any resemblance to actual persons, living or dead, events, or locales is entirely coincidental.

Published by George Franklin.
georgefranklinauthor.com
Atlanta, GA

Paperback ISBN: 978-1-7334444-4-6
Ebook ISBN: 978-1-7334444-5-3

Cover design and art direction by Julie Davis
Interior design by Liz Schreiter
Edited and produced by Reading List Editorial
ReadingListEditorial.com

Thanks to Kellogg. A world-class company that gave me the opportunity for a great run in Washington.

Also, to Becky O'Dell, who makes it all happen.

CHAPTER 1

He was a morally vacuous human being, but he came by it naturally. As a descendant of a long line of grifters, Mickey "Mick" Girtz was perfectly suited for a life in politics.

His father, State Senator Matt Girtz, was a Republican power broker in the Florida Senate in Tallahassee and a founding member of the infamous Pork Chop Gang, a group of elected officials identified as such in recognition of their ability to lather their districts with political pork under the rubric of free enterprise and competitive capitalism. They were also quite successful in lining their own pockets as they casually distributed the taxpayers' money.

Prior to entering politics, Matt Girtz owned and operated a used car lot called Girtz Storage where he sold previously wrecked, submerged, and abandoned vehicles, bought at auction, under the guise of them having been held in storage for now-deceased owners. Each auto was accompanied by a counterfeit death certificate as a means of authentication and to assure the buyer that he or she was getting a bargain. These business practices, however, often brought the ire of very much alive previous owners whose families would be the recipients of sympathy cards and condolences. It also garnered the attention of the Consumer Protection Division of the state attorney general, who sued Girtz Storage for "fraud, misrepresentation, and theft by deception."

Never one to be concerned with the facts, Matt categorized the lawsuit as just another attack on the free enterprise system and one more step toward socialism. He also, in order to thwart the further decline of America, announced his candidacy for the state senate as a Republican in what would be a hotly contested primary. His North Florida senate district encompassed the so-called "Redneck Riviera" area of Panama City up to the Georgia border. The last time a Democrat had won the seat was forty years prior when a candidate named George Wallace was mistaken for the former Alabama governor.

The Republican primary election was the name of the game, and Matt Girtz was facing a formidable opponent in Jack "Bubba" Thornbuckle. Not only did the nickname "Bubba" assure him the pickup truck vote, but he had been a star football player at Florida State University (FSU), which assured him the vote of every diehard Seminole fan within a hundred-mile radius. His signing to attend FSU had been a watershed moment in the national conversation about affirmative action for college athletes when the head coach declared, "Dadgummit, an inability to read and write should not impede a college education."

Matt immediately went on the offensive against Thornbuckle. He filed a lawsuit in Bay County District Court before a judge who had played for FSU's archrival, the University of Florida, seeking a declaratory judgment that Bubba was not his opponent's official name and enjoining the county election board from including it on the ballot. He also averred that allowing Bubba on the ballot would cast aspersions on an entire population of the Florida Panhandle and subject the region to ridicule by the liberal elite of Miami. After verifying that his alma mater, the University of Florida, had lost to FSU each year that Thornbuckle played, the judge ruled that the nickname "Bubba" be disallowed from the ballot.

The next offensive move by candidate Girtz was a game-changer. Scouring the voter rolls, Girtz's team found a ninety-four-year-old Korean War veteran named Jack Thornbuckle living in the Haven of Rest RV Park outside of Panama City. Matt's campaign brain trust determined that having another candidate with the same name as his primary opponent would split the Thornbuckle vote if they could get the veteran to run. They decided to approach him with a patriotic pitch that as a Korean War vet, he needed to heed the call of General Douglas McArthur, who famously declared, "I shall return," an exhortation that had nothing to do with the Korean War but resonated with him by getting his patriotic juices flowing so that he wanted to stand up for his country one more time. It was imperative that he run for the state senate; if he won, he would be the only member of the Korean War generation in that body. He finally agreed after being assured that Girtz's team would pay all the filing fees and campaign expenses and, oh by the way, would give his ne'er-do-well grandson a 1962 Chevy Corvair and a no-show job at the used car lot.

Matt Girtz won the primary in a squeaker:

> 36%—Matt Girtz
> 30%—Jack Thornbuckle
> 29%—Jack Thornbuckle
> 4%—Brenda Spurrier
> 1%—Muhammed Asbury

His opponent in the general election was a professor of environmental science at FSU, whose PhD dissertation was entitled, "How Tourism Will Destroy the Florida Panhandle." Matt trounced his Democratic opponent 84% to 16% and became a national example for the Republican Party of how free and fair elections always result in a Republican victory.

Now, after serving twenty-eight years, despite his initial promise of one term and out, Matt felt compelled to continue the family legacy of public service by creating a political opportunity for his son, Mickey.

At age thirty-one, Mickey was still finding himself. While Mickey was in high school, his father got him a job working for the Florida Department of Transportation counting cars. This arduous assignment involved him being dropped off on a remote country road with a counting clicker and a cooler of beer for the day. Sometimes as many as twelve cars would come by during a shift. The arduousness of this task was something that would impact his life forever. It was then that he came to realize honest work was highly overrated and that he would pursue a career in politics, a vocation that he liked to describe as involving "no heavy lifting."

Although he was a poor student, his father's position as a member of the senate's Higher Education Appropriations Committee assured him a spot in the freshman class of FSU. It was here that he began to assert himself. Maybe not the brightest bulb, but he was always lit.

His dorm room had a poster of his childhood hero, Chuck Colson, who had proclaimed he would run over his own grandmother to get President Nixon re-elected. He also had a picture of his current favorite, former governor Rod Blagojevich of Illinois, who was sent to the slammer for selling a US Senate seat. He regarded both men as emblematic of upstanding citizens who suffered from unwarranted attacks by the liberal media. Just another example of cancel culture at work; the careers of two distinguished statesmen had been ended.

Mickey's contrarian approach to college life extended into the social sphere. After being rejected by every single fraternity during rush, he formed the People Like Us (PLU) Club. The PLU Club emphasized the constitutional right to freedom of association and the right to deny membership under the "we sorts" philosophy of "we sorts" of people are different than "you sorts." The club consisted of Mick as President; John Wright IV, who was also the leader of the campus Ann Coulter Fan Club, as Vice-President; and Hans Schmidt, who had recently formed a new advocacy group, Justice for the Taliban, as Director of Diversity and Membership Recruitment.

Although small in numbers, the PLU Club immediately became a darling of right-wing media, especially One America News (OAN), which routinely featured Mick as the voice of the silent majority of college students. Mick would hark back to the days of Spiro Agnew, lamenting about whatever happened to the days when a politician could be bought and stay bought. His message that inclusion and diversity endangered the American/European ethos was especially powerful and resonated with the audience and earned him accolades as a myopic thinker, which was great praise coming from a listenership of Luddites. He was becoming a political force to be reckoned with.

As Mickey Girtz slowly became a cause célèbre, his father, Senator Matt Girtz, in the swan song of his career, was quietly going through the redistricting process, creating a new congressional district that would provide a political sinecure for his son for years to come.

CHAPTER 2

Pop-Tarts are a money machine for Kellogg Company. Introduced in 1964, millions are sold every year, making one wonder if there are really that many teenagers in America.

Annika Svensson never imagined she would be in charge of the marketing and manufacturing behemoth of Pop-Tarts within the Kellogg world. Growing up in International Falls, Minnesota, a town with the moniker "Ice Box of the Nation," she learned firsthand the meaning of the expression "like trying to sell ice to Eskimos." In her family's case, her father's attempt to sell frozen smoothies from a converted Good Humor truck in the frozen Minnesota winters and two weeks of summer fell flat.

Determined to make something of herself and expand her horizons, Annika attended St. Olaf College, where she majored in Nordic Studies, focusing on how a lack of diversity impacted the social and cultural mores of Scandinavia. One course that especially intrigued her covered the history of the Swedish meatball and how it impacted the nutritional profile of the region's indigenous people. This course essentially changed her life by creating an interest in food science and a fascination with how food consumption patterns could be used to affect demographic cultural control. After graduating from St. Olaf, she decided to pursue a master's degree and a PhD in Nutrition at the University of Wisconsin, where, with funding from the Dairy Council, she authored an award-winning article entitled, "How You Can Live on Cheese Alone."

The article, although controversial, catapulted her as a darling of the food industry while making her a pariah to the do-gooder, consumer advocacy world. One hyper-ventilating spokesperson for a food advocacy organization indignantly charged, "That woman could justify eating a park bench." A challenge that Annika accepted by creating a nutrient profile of pine bark, highlighting its high fiber content and how low it is in fat. This seminal work resulted in her being named Woman of the Year by the National Forestry Association, who then predicted that she would become the next Euell Gibbons.

Upon graduation from the University of Wisconsin, Annika took her first job in the food industry, and it was a tough one. Despite the company waving wads of cash at applicants, no one was willing to take it on. Everyone thought the role was a lost cause except Annika. It would make her renowned as a brand turnaround expert.

Hostess Twinkies had been a mainstay of children's lunch boxes since their inception in 1930. As cheap, sugar-filled gut bombs, they were a way for haggard mothers to placate screaming children. So what if they caused holy hell for teachers trying to control a room of kids buzzing on a sugar high. Most parents rationalized all of this by convincing each other that classroom chaos and unruly children were what teachers were paid to handle.

Sure, the brand took some barbs from the "nutrition police," but all was well until it took a significant hit from, of all things, a murder trial. The man accused of murdering the mayor of San Francisco invoked the "Twinkie defense," in which he argued that he suffered from "diminished capacity" as a result of an addiction to Twinkies. This novel defense resulted in the charges being lessened to manslaughter. Learning of this decision, thousands of failing students when facing expulsion or punishment would cite this precedent and argue diminished capacity from Twinkie consumption as a defense to mitigate any action by schools in response to failing grades or misconduct.

School boards around the country called emergency meetings to address the Twinkie crisis. Hundreds of crazed mothers in Birkenstocks, flowing dresses, and headbands descended on the meetings, demanding a ban on Twinkies. Tempers flared when some school board members had the temerity to recommend that parents simply quit buying Twinkies for their children. Screaming mothers would threaten bodily harm against the board members if they did not fulfill their duties as surrogate custodians entrusted with protecting children from their parents. The meetings were sheer bedlam, and the ensuing publicity put Twinkie sales into free fall.

When Annika entered the job market, the management of Twinkies was an unparalleled PR/nutrition nightmare. The situation required someone bold, daring, unflappable, and willing to distort and manipulate while creating alternative facts. They needed a Kellyanne Conway of the food world. Obfuscation and misdirection was the order of the day. This was a job for Annika Svensson.

Annika signed on as Vice-President, Consumer Engagement, Outreach, and Elucidation of Hostess Brands, and immediately began a campaign to resuscitate the Twinkie franchise. Her first move was to make a $1 million contribution to the Sugarcane Institute at the University of Florida School of Nutrition to document the positive connection between high sugar consumption and academic achievement. She then cleverly established a tie-in with Birkenstock and Twinkies wherein, with proof of purchase of six boxes of Twinkies, the consumer received 50% off the purchase price of a pair of Birkenstocks. This tie-in resulted in *Rolling Stone* magazine, in which Birkenstock was a major advertiser, publishing a feature article on how Twinkies were an integral component of the marijuana counterculture. Step three for Annika was to make another six-figure contribution, this time to the National Organization for the Promotion of Cannabis, with the understanding they would publicize the critical role of Twinkies in the satiation of munchies. Finally, she arranged for Twinkies to become the sole sponsor of happy hour at the National Association of School Boards in Las Vegas by funding a nightly open bar at the annual weeklong meeting.

Her multipronged attack became a prototype for the industry. The University of Florida study established a scientific firewall and even provided some justification for sugar consumption when it declared, "Strong evidence exists that Twinkie consumption on a daily basis may enhance cognitive skills." This new scientific evidence, combined with emerging lifestyle support from such socially conscious influencers as Birkenstock, *Rolling Stone*, and the marijuana movement, was clearly cooling the jets of Mothers Against Twinkies. A trend evidenced by a new Gallup poll showed Twinkies falling far behind climate change, going gluten-free, saving the whales, and supporting the Green New Deal as cocktail conversation topics among Progressives. Finally, as the chatter subsided and Twinkies became a non-issue, the National Association of School Boards passed a resolution recommending "a cessation of any Twinkie discussions until further examination of the scientific evidence can be completed and the sponsor of next year's happy hour at the convention has been determined."

The deft handling of the Twinkie imbroglio by Annika Svensson was not lost on the executives of Kellogg, who were concerned with the minacious social media buzz involving their Pop-Tarts cash cow. Any decline in Pop-Tart sales would significantly affect their annual bonuses, which was an untenable situation requiring immediate action.

CHAPTER 3

Elizabeth "Lizzie" Pendergast was of the manor born. Her parents, Clive and Olivia Pendergast, came from the upper crust of society in Newport, Rhode Island, and were a testament to the fact that your gene pool was more important than hard work. They, like most of their contemporaries, inherited their wealth and tried to instill in their children an appreciation for social structure, preordained prominence, and the need for the working class to remain industrious.

The Pendergast fortune was derived from Clive's grandfather, Clairborne Pendergast, who had successfully cornered the market of wooden spools for sewing threads. He did so by associating with Samuel Slater, who is regarded as the father of the American Industrial Revolution, though in his day, he was dubbed "Slater the Traitor" by the British. Turns out Samuel Slater had absconded from England with that nation's textile technology, which he used to set up a series of textile mills in the early 1800s in Rhode Island and throughout the northeast United States. Clairborne convinced Slater that he should be the sole supplier of wooden spools after Slater toured the Pendergast manufacturing facilities. Pendergast only employed children ages seven to twelve, who were paid a pittance and whose nimble fingers allowed them to avoid serious injury, at least most of the time, when extracting the wooden spools from the wood-carving machines. Slater found this management style impressive and reminiscent of his early career in England, where child labor was common and a means to make sure the next generation did not go soft.

Clairborne Pendergast made and sold millions of spools, which in turn made him a very rich man. After his departure from this earth, his family continued to enrich themselves through licensing agreements until wooden spools went the way of the buggy whip in the 1970s. The fortune, however, continued to grow and grow protected by a phalanx of lawyers and accountants, who created a series of trusts and offshore bank accounts to make sure no taxes were ever paid while investing in sweatshops in Bangladesh, in furtherance of the family legacy.

The family wealth of Clive and Olivia Pendergast allowed them to delve into the world of liberal Democratic politics. Their first major foray was hosting a book signing for Paul Welborn, a Brown University economics professor whose book *The Evil of Capitalism and Inherited Wealth* had made him a darling of the chic radical left. The event was not without controversy. Demonstrators arrived objecting to the Chablis, which had come from a vineyard that had taken action against farm worker unionization in California. This brouhaha was quickly dispelled when Clive announced to the demonstrators that in the future all wine served would be South African, thereby indirectly assisting the people's liberation movement. Although the demonstrators had no idea what the people were being liberated from, since post-apartheid South Africa was under Black majority rule, they figured, nevertheless, they must be liberated from something, so this would do.

The book signing was the first in a series of events at

their home for liberal causes. They became sort of an ATM for the far left. In addition to giving them something to do, Olivia Pendergast loved planning parties and events that put them in the spotlight, which they craved. *Vanity Fair* described them as "profound influencers" of the new avant-garde paradigm of political discourse, lacking only an Andy Warhol Campbell's soup can painting that was a staple of home décor for the "radical chic." They were in the forefront of places to be and be seen. The Pendergast family registered a ten on the Richter scale of political importance.

Little Lizzie was the poster child of a rich spoiled brat. She relished the political/cause-related gatherings at her parents' house, since guests would fawn over her as an obsequious gesture to her wealthy parents. After being told how cute and smart she was ad nauseam, she began to believe it, despite the fact she was frumpy, dumpy, and as they say in the movie biz, "Her face was not camera friendly."

Clive and Olivia found raising a child quite tedious and thought Lizzie would be better off at boarding school for high school with other children like her. So off to Choate boarding school in Connecticut she went, where she began to replicate her parents by becoming active in leftist causes. Her most notable involvement was with the student rights movement, which advocated the elimination of grades as a necessary first step in the creation of a classless society. In pursuit of this cause, she led a sit-in at the President's office, where they survived on croissants and lattes for two days—two days welcomed by the dorm maid service, as this time allowed them to do a deep clean while students camped out in the administration lobby. Although the President refused to eliminate grades, the students considered it a victory when the chancellor of Choate announced that henceforth crepes would be available for breakfast in all the school cafeterias.

Although a mediocre student at Choate, Lizzie applied to the prestigious Brown University and was accepted under the Legacy Scholars program, which her grandfather had endowed. It was at Brown that she blossomed and where her penchant for activism was a natural fit. The university was the birthplace of woke. Freedom of speech and expression was encouraged so long as it didn't make anyone uncomfortable. Political discourse was accepted so long as it was consistent with liberal orthodoxy, and anything to the contrary was banned as corrosive to free thought, meaningful discourse, and academic freedom.

The strictures on political thought and activity did not sit well with local Democratic congressman Joe O'Brien. He came from a blue-collar labor union background and knew that appearing before the new-wave student forum of which Lizzie was commandant would be dicey. The students looked perplexed when he called for the creation of good-paying union jobs. He was challenged to answer when one student screamed out, "Why do you need jobs when people have trust funds?" He enraged all those in attendance when he suggested that many Republicans were good people and that compromise might be necessary to accomplish some objectives. He further inflamed the students when questioned about climate change by calling it all liberal political poppycock while refusing to co-sponsor legislation that would "ban cars and planes until solar-powered alternatives are developed."

The final straw, however, was when he referred to native Alaskans as Eskimos while declining to endorse reparations for them, even after the program moderator explained that as indigenous people of Alaska they would suffer irreparable harm from climate change and that it could be funded by an excise tax on refrigerators. His response sent the assembled students into a state of spasmodic convulsions and apoplectic disbelief. Lizzie stood on her chair and began leading the chant, "DINO, DINO, DINO!"—Democrat in Name Only—while waving a red bandanna embossed with a hammer and sickle. The congressman, fearing for his safety, skedaddled out the back door but before doing so gave the crowd his middle finger. It was now pandemonium. The crowd was in a state of hyper-hysteria. Soon the chant went from "DINO" to "Lizzie, Lizzie, Lizzie." This was her Reichstag moment. Lizzie was being called on to run for Congress and lead a movement. In her mind, this was her date with destiny.

CHAPTER 4

In the McDonell family, the country refrain "You know a bad day of fishing beats a good day of anything else" was gospel. Everybody in the family loved fishing. When Skipper McDonell wasn't at his job at Waffle House or tending to the small family farm in North Georgia, he was out fishing. Pretty much the same for his wife, Bobbi Jo, who, when not working in the quilting department of Hobby Lobby or canning jams and jellies, was out fishing. Even her clothes displayed her love of fishing. Her favorite T-shirt was emblazoned with "Some girls dance on poles. Real girls fish with them." This shared love of fishing resulted in the name Skipper and Bobbi Jo chose for their oops baby, Rod, since his arrival meant one less fishing rod they could afford.

As a young tyke, Rod inherited the family's passion for fishing. A poor student with few outside interests other than fishing, he might have been considered somewhat of a loser, except for the fact that he was a very good fisherman. Starting in his late teens and into his early twenties, he routinely won practically every fishing contest in North Georgia and western North Carolina. Whether it was Lake Rabun, Lake Burton, Lake Glenville, or hundreds of streams and rivers throughout the area, he always managed to catch the biggest and the most. He attributed his success to crickets. Yes, crickets, but not just any cricket. The only crickets he would use as bait had to come from Ghann's

Cricket Farm outside of Augusta, Georgia. In business since 1952, Ghann's is a family-owned and operated business that is arguably the largest producer of crickets for bait in the United States, producing to the tune of three million crickets per week. Rod swore by the quality of the crickets and agreed with the claim on Ghann's website that they were "clean, healthy, lively" critters and irresistible to any fish. They were the cocaine of the fish world.

As Rod's reputation spread on the fishing circuit, he became known as the "Cricket Man." This nickname caught the attention of Cricket Wireless, which became his principal sponsor, plastering logos all over his clothes and boat, making him look like a NASCAR driver. The buzz about him on social media also caught the attention of the Entomological Society of America, which at its annual convention awarded him their highest honor, "Bug Man of the Year." Recognition that came with a monogrammed beekeeper's hat, a year's supply of Off repellent, and a DVD of Walt Disney's 1968 hit movie *The Love Bug*.

That same year, during the evening cocktail party sponsored by Orkin, Rod met the DC lobbyist for the Entomological Society, P. J. "Snakeboots" Jackson. Snakeboots had attended the University of Georgia, where he majored in agriculture and public policy, before attending law school at that same institution, where he acquired the nickname "Snakeboots" in recognition of his distinctive footwear. He had a closet full of boots made from snakeskins, which he specially ordered from Rocketbuster in El Paso, Texas, which was world-renowned for handmade custom boots. Cobra, rattle, python, you name it, but his favorite was a pair made from copperheads because, as he was fond of saying, "They were quick to bite." Upon graduation from law school, he went to work for US senator Herman Talladeor of Georgia, who was a member of the Senate Agriculture Committee and generally regarded as a wholly owned subsidiary of the peanut and cotton industry. Snakeboots's official title was legislative aide, but he was also known in the office as a payment transfer specialist, which meant he was the conduit for speaking fees, i.e. honorariums, earned by the senator for being the guest speaker at numerous peanut and cotton association events around the state. It didn't matter that often the "audience" would be comprised of only three or four people and that it was the same speech every time. He was paid handsomely for those appearances, not to mention the free accommodations, food, and drinks at luxurious resorts for him and his confidential assistant.

Snakeboots held this critically important and sensitive position until the good senator was indicted and convicted by a Department of Justice task force investigating public corruption and money laundering in the public sector. His goose was cooked when his jilted wife reported that he kept wads of cash from unnamed sources in the pockets of the overcoats hanging in his hall closet. The senator copped a plea by agreeing to resign "in the interest of the citizens of Georgia," but all the while claiming that this was all a political vendetta by the liberal media and those people in Atlanta.

The senator's demise meant the end of Snakeboots's meal ticket, requiring a quick career pivot. He hung out his shingle as a lobbyist specializing in earmarks and good government and was immediately retained by the peanut industry and cotton growers. It was during the Cotton Growers Association's annual Boll Weevil Ball that he met the President of the Entomological Society and signed them up as a client.

Huddled over a couple of Grasshopper cocktails, the official drink of the society, Rod and Snakeboots went from exchanging pleasantries into an earnest conversation about future business dealings. Rod knew that his primary source of income as a world champion fisherman had a limited life span. This was true for every sports celebrity, and the smart ones used their status to diversify into sundry businesses while their glam factor still opened doors and wallets. By Rod's thinking, he had two significant assets. The first was his fishing skill, but, as mentioned, he knew it had a limited shelf life in a very crowded sector. The other, less substantive asset was his trademark nickname, Cricket Man. He had parlayed that into a sponsorship from Cricket Wireless, but he was realistic enough to recognize that as his fishing prowess declined, he would eventually be considered as useless as a sundial in the shade.

As Rod mulled over his predicament with Snakeboots, the lobbyist's fertile mind went into overdrive. He had just left a presentation at the Entomological Convention entitled, "Bugs: If You Can't Beat 'Em, Eat 'Em." The presentation included slides from the European International Platform of Insects for Food and Feed, detailing how insects were a good source of fiber, iron, and calcium, as well as protein, and that they provided these nutritional attributes with a low carbon footprint. Snakeboots wasn't known as the Svengali of spin for nothing. Looking Rod dead in the eye, he proposed that they collaborate on the creation of a National Cricket Consortium, which would be a series of cricket farms to feed a hungry planet. Cricket farms touched every political hot button. European competition positioned them as a national security issue. A low carbon footprint made them an integral aspect of the fight against climate change, and their nutritional profile placed them squarely in the battle against childhood obesity. Finally, their presence in rural communities would create thousands of new jobs and revitalize farm towns desperate for new industries. Snakeboots concluded by envisioning that cricket food would be the hottest topic at every cocktail party attended by the silk stocking crowd and would stir natterings among cultural nabobs and the Progressive clerisy. Oprah, Rachel Maddow, Anderson Cooper, Fareed Zakaria, and other luminaries would clamor for a National Cricket consortium to address the burgeoning need for action against the aforementioned maladies of the world.

Hearing all this from Snakeboots had Rod's head spinning. He was very persuasive, and Rod found himself getting caught up in the fervor of the pitch. Rod, however, had a practical side, and as his granddaddy used to say, "This was a little too much sugar for a dime."

Looking Snakeboots straight in the eye, Cricket Man asked, "How are we going to pay for all this?"

To which Snakeboots responded, without missing a beat, "That is why God made the government."

CHAPTER 5

She was a precocious little brat who evolved into boorishness as a young woman, a transition that came as no surprise to anyone who had watched her upbringing.

Born to well-to-do parents in Demorest, Georgia, Barb Breen had a silver spoon firmly implanted in her mouth and the undivided attention of her doting parents, as is often the case with an only child. Her situation, however, took spoiled to another level. Her father, Roger Breen, was given the family road-building business by his father shortly after graduating from the University of Georgia. During his long, six-year slog through undergrad, Roger was the platonic ideal of a frat boy. A member of the Alpha Tau Omega fraternity, he was the chapter delegate to the Interfraternity Council and a rabid UGA football fan, bordering on obsessive. Widely regarded as a "big man" on campus, he was a sought-after catch by husband-hunting co-eds until he was "pinned" with Peetsy Broadchurch, a UGA cheerleader and member of the Alpha Chi Omega sorority. They were the Ken and Barbie of the UGA social set.

Married shortly before graduation and armed with his degree in Entrepreneurship and hers in Philanthropy, they moved to Demorest so he could join the family business, or claim his birthright, as he liked to say. His no-show job in the business world allowed him to become active in civic affairs as chair of the local Republican Party and Peetsy to decline employment, which she claimed would be a distraction from her philanthropic endeavors with the Junior League. Roger assumed the chairmanship of the Coalition to Stop Government Spending, and Peetsy ascended to become the honorary chair of the Festival of Lights Christmas fundraiser. These two positions certified their status as the power couple of Demorest, Georgia.

As their social status soared, the family business thrived. The company's road-building projects grew exponentially after Roger's fraternity brother became Director of the Georgia Department of Transportation with the ability to issue a series of noncompete contracts to pave hundreds of miles of essentially unused roads under the department's Rural Development program. Roger reciprocated the Director's largesse by making available to him the company jet, so that he and his Hooters waitress paramour could attend every UGA away football game.

Life was good for the Breens, and especially after they were blessed with the arrival of their daughter, Barb. She was a cute little thing, but you would think she was the next Shirley Temple the way they fawned over her. When she was six months old, they submitted her photo to the Beautiful Baby contest at the Georgia State Fair. When notified that she had come in third, behind Busaba Ananada, an immigrant from Thailand, and Daryna Shevchenko, a Ukrainian war refugee, Peetsy went ballistic, venting on Facebook that the only reason Barb had not won was that "woke culture was running amok in North Georgia." A few years later, they entered her into the Preteen Miss Sassy Sweetheart contest at Unicoi State Park, where she placed fourth. Once again, Peetsy went off the rails, citing the fact that the third-place finisher, who was of Vietnamese descent, was proof that a sea barrier needed to be built to prevent the dilution of European ethnic centricity by Asian immigrants. When reminded that the first- and second-place finishers were named O'Reilly and Jones, she retorted that they were proof of runaway "tokenism." The last straw was when Barb failed to make the high school cheerleading squad, which included two African American students. Peetsy organized a team of supporters from the wives of the men who worked for her husband and stormed the school board meeting with placards demanding "Justice for Barb" and "Down with CRT."

The media went into overdrive when asked what CRT—Critical Race Theory—had to do with the issue, since it was not taught in Demorest schools. Peetsy attacked the question as an attempt by the lamestream media to deflect the core issue of "reverse discrimination." She then went on to warn all assembled that the next thing you know there would be mandatory twerking classes for cheerleaders, creating a squad of hoochie mamas. Her dire warnings sent the assembled parents into a rage, screaming for the school board to be recalled and defunded. It was total bedlam. The chair summarily ended the meeting by declaring a public safety emergency.

Once again, the national media pounced. This was a ratings gift horse. Don Lemon of CNN, close to tears, intoned that North Georgia was returning to an era of white robes and torches, only this time it was sign-carrying, crazed mothers. The network then announced an upcoming special documentary, *The KKK Rides Again—Flames of Terror in the South*.

Tucker Carlson of Fox News forewarned that this whole episode was the result of a national trend toward group identity and a quota system. It was, as he saw it, a systematic plot being organized by the deep state, outlined on Hunter Biden's laptop.

Ironically, the whole kerfuffle was fulfilling the dream of the Breen family by making Barb the center of national attention. Some people loathed her, but what the hell, fame was fame. A nobody from nowhere had become somebody, and Barb relished the notoriety. It didn't matter that substantively she had accomplished nothing or that her parents had accomplished nothing on their own. The family road to success was a product of their birthright. Barb was like a Kardashian or Paris Hilton, famous because she was famous, and fame was a currency to be exploited.

CHAPTER 6

Clyde Cartwright had come a long way from the family farm where he grew up in Ames, Iowa. The son of a pig farmer and self-declared "meat guy," he was fulfilling a dream when he became Executive Director of the National Hot Dog and Sausage Council in Washington, DC. Now he was a power broker for the industry he loved and was able to influence public policy so that pig farmers got their fair share of government pork.

There are about 5,400 pig farms in Iowa, with fourteen to fifteen million pigs residing in the state at any one time. Considering the state has a human population of slightly over three million people, the swine could run the place if they could vote. However, since they can't, they indirectly run the place through their economic impact. Iowa is the only place where referring to a pigsty is a compliment.

Clyde's life from an early stage revolved around pigs. His first kid joke was "What is a pig's favorite karate move? A pork chop." And it went on from there. Miss Piggy was his fold-out calendar girl, and his favorite Hollywood star was Meathead, the son-in-law of Archie Bunker in the sitcom *All in the Family*. Clyde considered the sobriquet of "Meathead" to be a most honorific identification. His superhero, however, was Joey Chestnut, the repeat winner of the annual Nathan's Hot Dog Eating Contest. In Clyde's estimation, anyone who could eat seventy-six hot dogs and buns in ten minutes was a national treasure and not a mere mortal. He would never forget his father reflecting wistfully that if only the rest of America could and would do what Joey did, just imagine how pork prices would spike.

Clyde was clearly different than your typical teenage boy. Most teenagers played video games like *Call of Duty*, *NBA 2K20*, and *Madden NFL*. Not Clyde. He repeatedly watched the 4-H pig farming simulator on YouTube while also studying the breeding techniques used to create Reggie, the 1,335-pound swine that won the fattest pig at the Iowa State Fair.

His preoccupation with all matters concerning pork reached a crescendo when the Wienermobile rolled into Ames, an event so exciting that he skipped his Poultry as an Alternative nutrition lecture to make sure he was able to secure a prime viewing spot downtown.

The iconic Wienermobile dates back to 1936, when Oscar Mayer's nephew Carl dreamed up this marketing gimmick. He placed a replica of a giant hot dog on a specially built vehicle chassis. The Wienermobile's midget driver (now, in deference to political correctness, called a little person) was appropriately named Little Oscar. The Wienermobile would travel from town to town, blasting out the wiener jingle with Little Oscar doling out wiener whistles and other trinkets. It was pure Americana.

The turnout in Ames for the Wienermobile exceeded even the parade for the Miss Piglet beauty contest at the state fair. Families with little tykes jostled to snag the swag being tossed out by a slightly inebriated little person in a chef's hat and culinary garb. The excitement was palpable.

This was, without a doubt, the most exciting day of

Clyde's young life and reinforced in him a burning desire to pursue a career in the edible animal industry. To him, the word *vegetarian* was just an old Sioux word meaning "lousy hunter." This day validated what he knew in his gut was to be his calling. He would become a relentless advocate for animal agriculture until bacon, ham, pork chops, and the almighty hot dog were given the recognition they were due.

In order to attain these lofty aspirations, Clyde concluded that a college degree would come in handy. He decided to stay local, enrolled in Iowa State University (ISU) right there in Ames, and began to pursue a dual degree in Animal Management and Marketing Livestock. He also figured it would be a deft move to join Alpha Gamma Rho, the National Agricultural Fraternity, where he could make critical political contacts.

All was copacetic until one day, crossing campus, he came upon a couple sitting behind a card table smoking grass with a banner declaring, *Why do we need farmers as long as we have grocery stores? Join the Animal Legal Defense Fund.*

The two, Stardust Magellan and Yardley Thomas, looked like cast members of the sixties tribal rock love musical *Hair*, with tie-dyed shirts, long, stringy hair, camo pants, berets à la Che Guevara, and sandals made from recycled tires. They were to Clyde alien beings who had somehow landed on the ISU campus, and Clyde was horrified. Their presence was sacrilegious. They were in the palace of pork. It brought to mind his Bible studies, during which he'd heard the story of Jesus chasing the money changers out of the temple. Clyde would do the same.

He grabbed a couple of pamphlets from the table and retreated to the fraternity house to review what they were pitching. He was aghast. The first handout, entitled, "The Animal Rights Manifesto," called for an end to "speciesism" and the creation of a world where humans and other animals could live in peace without one species dominating another. It went on to demand legal rights for animals, including the ability of animals to pursue class-action lawsuits against farmers as well as free public housing and food stamps for all animals subject to factory farming. The second pamphlet, entitled, "A Call to Action," advocated for civil disobedience in front of and in any grocery store that sold hamburger, hot dogs, pork chops, chicken wings, or foie gras. Activists were encouraged to come dressed as chickens, pigs, and cows, lie down inside the meat counter, steal grocery carts, and create safe zones around the meat alternative section of the store, where customers could shop without being pestered or harassed.

Clyde could not believe what he was reading. This was a direct assault on his way of life and everything he cherished. If there was ever a call to arms by the animal agriculture industry, this was it. Someone needed to counterattack these misfits, and he had a plan.

That night, after eight pitchers of beer at the Last Chance Lounge, Clyde and six of his fraternity brothers from Alpha Gamma Rho sprang into action. They first went dumpster diving behind a recently condemned Chinese restaurant to retrieve decaying pork, chicken, beef, egg rolls, and dumplings. They strategically placed this rancid food in and around the table where Stardust and Yardley would be seated in the morning. They then broke into the university's animal testing lab with a portable mesh chicken coop, which they filled with thirty or so rats that were under long-term observation to see how long rats could live without food or water. They completed the night by placing the rat-filled coops in bushes about ten feet behind the activists' table and devised a rope that when pulled would allow the rats to escape.

It just so happened that the next morning a local TV station was there to interview the two animal rights activists as part of a series called *Courage on Campus*, a periodic program that the week before had highlighted members of the Coalition Against Mechanized Farming, which advocated a return to horse-drawn plows to combat climate change. Just as Stardust began to expound on how all animals have rights equal to humans, Clyde yanked the rope, allowing over thirty starved rats to make a mad rush for the decaying food. It was pandemonium, all caught live on television. Hysterical screams were followed by panic. The table was overturned and the banner shredded as Stardust and Yardley fled the scene. The local TV camera managed to keep rolling, showing terrified students running in horror while texting that the campus was being overrun with rodents. The President of the university ordered a campus-wide lockdown until a rapacious rat reduction plan could be devised and implemented. It was total bedlam.

Meanwhile, Clyde and his buddies became local heroes in the Ames farming community. They had humiliated the hippie agitators and stood up for the Ames way of life. It was predicted that Clyde would go a long way. He might even go all the way to Washington.

Stardust and Yardley, suffering from embarrassment and ridicule, slunk away from ISU. It was not, however, the last Clyde Cartwright would hear from them.

YEARS LATER

CHAPTER 7

Article I, Section 2 of the United States Constitution sets a term of office of two years for members of the House of Representatives, and newly elected representatives constitute a new Congress every two years. In other words, they have to start all over.

The 118th Congress convened in January 2023 and attempted to start procedurally, the same as every other Congress, but its new members proved to be problematic. A new Congress is called to order by the clerk, who then leads the Pledge of Allegiance, followed by the chaplain, who recites a prayer for the members, but in this instance, after looking at the members, the chaplain decided to pray for the country.

The first order of business is to elect a Speaker, usually a preordained party-line vote that is devoid of theatrics, but not when Kevin McCrudy, the Republican, was seeking the position with a slim five-vote majority. When the vote was announced, a newly elected Republican member from Georgia, i.e., a newbie, stood on the backbench, hurling outlandish claims that the election was fraudulent, stolen, illegitimate, and the result of a conspiracy of foreign operatives working to undermine American democracy by rigging the House vote tally machines. This outburst stunned the clerk, who then demanded a show of hands so that each vote could be individually counted. This exercise, involving all 435 members, confirmed the accuracy of the previous vote but was again rejected by the member from Georgia, who pronounced that such a result was an outgrowth of "new math" being taught in schools. Barb Breen of Georgia had made quite a splash on her first day in Congress.

Despite the brouhaha over his election, Speaker McCrudy took the gavel and administered the Oath of Office to the assembled members of Congress. He then, as is normal, moved that the House adopt a set of rules to govern operational procedures. Normally rules are adopted with a non-controversial party-line vote, but not this time around. On this occasion, the fly in the ointment was another member of his own party, Mickey Girtz, a Republican from Florida, and another newbie who threw a tantrum. He was the de facto leader of a loosely organized group that identified itself as the Freedom Fighters. To them, *compromise* was just another word for sellout, and decorum imposed by rules was merely another means of subjugation by the swamp cartel.

The member from Florida sauntered to the well of the House chambers and announced the Freedom Fighters would withhold their votes for the rules unless their demands were met.

- Hunter Biden's laptop and President Biden's Corvette should be confiscated as material components of a crime scene and sold on eBay to lower the national debt.
- A wall should be built on the Canadian border to prevent any roundabout entry by illegals from Mexico.

- Litter boxes should be banned from schools to deter students from identifying as animals.
- Members of Congress should be limited to one term.
- National divorce proceedings should commence immediately to separate Red and Blue states.

The Speaker, anxious to avoid a political train wreck, hastily called for a recess and convened a meeting with the Freedom Fighters to discuss their demands. The other members of the Republican caucus anxiously awaited the outcome, while the Democratic leadership did interviews on CNN and MSNBC, proclaiming that the dysfunction of the Republican Party portended imminent economic collapse, chaos in Congress, and a return to the gold standard.

After what felt like an eternity, the Speaker and the Freedom Fighters called a press conference to announce the details of an accommodation that had been reached.

Henceforth:

- A GoFundMe site would be established to raise as much or more money than might be raised by the sale of Hunter Biden's laptop and his dad's Corvette.
- Billboards would be built on the Mexican side of the border advertising the average winter temperature in Canada with the admonition *Frio!*
- Any child identifying as an animal would be required to carry a pooper scooper.
- Members of Congress could stay for more than one term if their father refused to take them back into the family business.

- Divorce proceedings would be placed on hold until property rights to nuclear warheads could be adjudicated.

Following the adoption of the rules, the last and arguably most significant step in organizing a new Congress is assigning each member to committees. Political careers can be made or broken by this process, and it is closely followed by the lobbying community, which tracks where friend or foe ends up.

There are twenty so-called "standing committees," plus five select and four joint, which carry with them degrees of influence, impact, and fundraising opportunities. Agriculture, Appropriations, and Energy and Commerce carry more weight than Small Business, Veterans Affairs, and House Administration. Normally each party caucus determines the placement of their members on committees without interference from whoever wields the Speaker's gavel. In the 118th Congress, however, Speaker Kevin McCrudy rejected the placement of a Democrat freshman from Rhode Island, Liz Pendergast, on any major committee and banished her to the House Committee on Administration and the political obscurity of the Joint Committee on Printing. This had the lobbyist community abuzz and, along with the chaotic Speaker's election and the mini mutiny over the rules, indicated that the 118th Congress would be a strange one indeed.

All the inside baseball of Congress was not lost on P. J. "Snakeboots" Jackson, who was ensconced in his elaborate K Street office. Widely regarded as the most powerful lobbyist in DC, he had a network of sources that kept him apprised of the comings and goings of every member of Congress. Just a few years before, he had been a lowly senate staffer for the besmirched former senator from Georgia, Herman Talladeor. Now he owned and operated the most influential public advocacy shop in town. He had built it through gall and guile, armed with a political action committee that was unrivaled by any of his competitors. His braggadocio came through in an interview with the *New York Times*, where he was asked whether he was concerned about a change in power in Washington, to which he responded, "I am ready for anything barring a military coup, and give me twenty-four hours, and I will be ready for that."

Snakeboots understood that information as to what made members tick was a source of power and leverage. He needed to know more about the three upstarts behind the Speaker's election imbroglio, the rules flap, and the political neutering of the freshman from Rhode Island. He sent his minions out to get the skinny behind the lead story.

Turns out Barb Breen, the audacious young woman from Georgia who challenged the Speaker's election, represented a ruby-red district in the northern part of the state. Considered the diva of disinformation by the mainstream Republican Party, she promoted herself as a businesswoman but failed to mention that her position in the family road-building business was simply intended to provide her income. She had become a darling of Fox News at an early age, when she was the focus of a riotous school board meeting over her failure to make the high school cheerleading squad. Her mother had led the assault on the board meeting, declaring that what had happened to her daughter was a case of reverse discrimination and an attack on

"Southern heritage and the legacy of Scarlett O'Hara." This newfound notoriety and fame catapulted her into a career as a television pitchwoman. Decked out in a low-cut tank top, miniskirt, and four-inch heels, she hustled, "Clyde's Convenience Store: Where Whiskey, Guns, Ammo, and Everything You Need Is in One Spot" and "Harry's Animal Center: Veterinarian/Taxidermist—Either Way You Get Your Dog Back."

She was a household name in North Georgia, but what really solidified her position as the candidate to beat was her presence on the local radio station's morning farm report. It was on this show that she announced that a rash of forest fires in the area had actually been started by climate activists using drone-directed lasers to stoke eco-anxiety in the state. This revelation resulted in a march on the National Forest Service regional headquarters, during which Smokey the Bear was hung in effigy.

There was a groundswell encouraging her to enter the Congressional race, and when she did, she was a dogged campaigner. She easily captured the Republican nomination and campaigned in the general election against her Democratic opponent in a borrowed, battered pickup truck, charging her opponent was a "known thespian," eliciting gasps from the assembled. She won in a landslide and was off to Washington to challenge everybody and everything, including members of her own party who had the temerity to question her absolutism.

After a bit of political sleuthing, Snakeboots figured out what was behind the election of Elizabeth "Lizzie" Pendergast of Rhode Island, who had been banished to the backwater of committee assignments. He was aware of her highly publicized upset victory over the supposedly entrenched Democratic congressman Joe O'Brien in the primary. Joe had been so unconcerned by her candidacy that the week before the election he went on a golfing junket in Miami sponsored by Hooters and the National Association of Beer Wholesalers. Even when pictures of his dalliance on the beach with Miss Hooter of the Year went viral, he still regarded the race as a sure thing.

Lizzie's victory was a stunning rebuke of the Democratic national leadership and became a bellwether for the Progressive movement. Her path to victory became a roadmap for upending the party power structure. During college at Brown University, she created a persona as a take-no-prisoners firebrand by becoming an outspoken advocate for reparations for native Alaskans, who, as indigenous people of the northern tundra, would suffer the most from climate change. This activism in turn introduced her to the allyship movement in Providence, where she lived in a wing of her parents' mansion. Since allyship requires supporting other social identity groups and individuals, she converted the servants' quarters in her parents' home into a safe space where she would hold weekly confabs with marginalized groups. It was under her auspices that disparate identity organizations such as Dogwalkers United, the Coalition for Janitor Rights, the Sisterhood of the Socially Unacceptable, and the Coalition of Misunderstood Millennials would meet in a safe, nurturing, and unchallenged environment to discuss their plight.

During these confabs, they found a leader in Lizzie. She proclaimed that anybody who has sung "The Star-Spangled Banner" knows America is the land of the free, and therefore it was only reasonable that Congress fulfill this promise by making stuff they wanted for free. She assured each group that if elected to Congress, she would introduce legislation to create temporary programs to make sure they got their share of free whatever. When challenged why "temporary," she reminded them that there was nothing more permanent than a temporary government program. She had a committed following. She swamped the incumbent in the primary and overwhelmed her Republican opponent in the general election, labeling him as un-American, since he had the gall to suggest citizens pay for things in the "land of the free."

One last important piece of information: Snakeboots had to find out why this nobody newbie from Rhode Island, Lizzie Pendergast, had been tossed into the trash bin of political obscurity. Being assigned to the Committee on House Administration and the Joint Committee on Printing was the legislative equivalent of being sent to the Russian front. Clearly, she had gotten crosswise with the leadership, so he contacted a source in the Rhode Island Governor's Office who was in charge of political gaslighting and anti-vaxxer outreach to get the dope on what had gone on.

The first thing up was that young Lizzie was the ne'er-do-well daughter of rich parents who were ne'er-do-well children of rich parents themselves. Lizzie, whose personal professional accomplishments were nil, found herself in a tough general election battle and needed an issue to call her own, to differentiate herself from her opponent. She instructed her campaign research assistant, who had previously served as chief fact-checker in the John Kerry campaign before the swift boat ads, to conduct a systematic review of MeWe.com and Gettr.com, the new conservative social media sites, to see what was trending.

Sure enough, on an old Obama birther site, she found a claim that would definitely excite her base. The allegation was that Speaker McCrudy's family had illegally entered the country and that therefore he was shanty Irish and a mick, and as such was suspect as to his acumen, work ethic, and drinking habits along with numerous unmentioned tawdry traits, making him problematic as Speaker. Now, it might seem counterintuitive that an unabashed lefty would refer to someone as a "mick" and question their birthright. Tactically, however, it was brilliant. It worked in her whisper campaign against O'Brien, her primary opponent, who was disdained by her supporters, and would keep them energized by conflating O'Brien and McCrudy. Needless to say, calling him a "mick" sent the Irish American Anti-Defamation League into overdrive. They really went ballistic when the Pendergast campaign declared, "Not only was he a poster child for immigration reform, he couldn't run a gin mill, much less the House of Representatives." Irish Americans throughout the country went apoplectic, and the National Bartenders Union issued a statement decrying her statement as racist and accusing her of stereotyping the 95% of their members who were Irish. Politically, however, in her district, the issue was a gold mine. She offered proof that she was not anti-Irish, citing as evidence that she had Irish maids growing up, considered beer a proletariat beverage but okay on St. Patrick's Day, and had twice seen the Irish musical *Riverdance* on Broadway. She also did a master pivot, with a little bit of whataboutism, when she challenged her audience to think about what all this really mattered when you considered how few

Irish Americans fought in the Civil War!

Speaker McCrudy watched from afar all those goings-on in the Pendergast campaign. He kept his powder dry during the fall campaign, hoping against hope that Pendergast would lose, but when she won, he knew how to extract his revenge. Meaner than a junkyard dog, he let it be known among his colleagues that anything with Pendergast's name on it was DOA. Her committee assignments were only the beginning.

A good lobbyist knows how to play their cards, and Breen, Pendergast, and Girtz were three new ones in the DC political deck. Snakeboots had a habit of crooning a song he had written to the tune of "The Gambler" by Kenny Rogers. It was his creed.

> The secret to thriving is knowing who to fund
> and when to make them run.
> You just got to know what you told 'em
> Know when to scold 'em
> Or just tell them to walk away.
> Cause every pol has a price
> And a role to play
> They are there for the asking
> Win, lose, or draw.

Unbeknownst to the three newbies—Girtz, Breen, and Pendergast—they were simply cards in a deck to be shuffled and dealt, then held, discarded, or folded as needed by the master political poker player, the one and only Snakeboots Jackson.

CHAPTER 8

The boys in corporate headquarters in Battle Creek were in a panic. Sales of Pop-Tarts had flat-lined and were even dropping, and no additional marketing seemed able to turn it around.

Russ Magpie, the new Kellogg CEO, was hell-bent on preventing the deterioration of this iconic brand under his watch. His response to any criticism of company failings was that he was "positioning the company for growth," which was an indecipherable response to most analysts but bought him time with the company's board of directors. How plummeting Pop-Tart sales had anything to do with company positioning was corporate gobbledygook, earning Magpie a sobriquet within the company, "Master of Obfuscation."

He tried every marketing and sales trick in the book. The company virtually carpet-bombed the trade with coupons, but to no avail. He then went the BOGO (Buy One, Get One Free) route, which did increase volume, but at the expense of the bottom line, since this meant essentially giving the product away. Finally, he tried the time-tested approach of a price cut, which boomeranged by creating a social media stir generated by the Center for Science in Our Own Interest consumer group, which charged that, whatever the cost, Pop-Tarts were too expensive for your health. In a nutshell, the product was in a PR/marketing/

sales nosedive, and even with a tsunami of spin, everyone knew it.

These troublesome developments resulted in the company CFO alerting Russ he was alarmed at the disturbing possibility that the executive stock option plan could take a significant hit. Russ realized dramatic action was in order and called for an emergency two-day off-site meeting at the Four Seasons in Hawaii to discuss synergistic optimization of Pop-Tarts branding by exploring new paradigms available in alternative sales channels and cutting-edge, proactive marketing techniques. When questioned by the corporate controller about the cost of such a meeting, which included cranking up two Falcon 900 jets, twenty-eight rooms at the Four Seasons, and a welcome luau party featuring a Don Ho imitator with "Welcome to Paradise" gift bags, Russ was incredulous. Everyone knew that positioning for growth was an expensive proposition and that January in Battle Creek, Michigan, was too cold for critical thinking.

Sixteen consultants joined the meeting in order to conduct breakout sessions on such topics as value-added, taking ownership, low-hanging fruit, and onboarding. All in all, the meeting was deemed a success with the weather in the low eighties, two afternoon golf breaks, and a deep-sea fishing trip that bagged three marlins and a tuna. As far as the Pop-Tarts were concerned, the conclusion of the meeting was that "slumping sales warranted continued vigilance."

The consumer group attack initiated by the Center for Science in Our Own Interest spread through the food police advocacy world. The National Nanny Network attacked the product as containing too many calories, too much sugar and fat, and lacking any positive nutritional attributes. The company struck back by claiming that if it was up to the do-gooders, children would only be allowed to eat Brussels sprouts and tofu and that the leadership of the Center and the Nanny Network should check into a "woke detox center."

The nutritional controversy surrounding Pop-Tarts became further clouded when a group of agitated consumers prodded by a law firm recruiting clients on cable TV with a call-in number—1-800-Get-Cash—filed a $5 million class-action lawsuit claiming the product contained "fruit fiction." The basis of the case was that the fruit content was so minimal as to render any fruit claim to be "false, deceptive, and misleading." The media reaction was modest but became inflamed when the company's general counsel was quoted as saying, in exasperation, "People have to learn how to take a joke." The statement set off a barrage of anti-lawyer jokes on social media; the company's general counsel was described as the "soupcon shyster," all of which further eroded the brand's image. The company was in serious damage control.

After returning from Hawaii and a two-week skiing stopover in Aspen, CEO Magpie called a meeting of his brain trust to discuss what to do about Pop-Tarts. They gathered in the fifth-floor War Room with six new consultants to strategize over "out of the box" thinking, a term they had learned in Hawaii, proving the worth of the $1.2 million corporate getaway.

Leading the discussion was Dirk Dantley, an executive with the ad firm Gray Fog, Inc., who handled the multimillion-dollar Pop-Tarts account. Dirk was considered an outside, independent arbiter who could be counted on to place blame for the demise of the brand anywhere but on the assembled executives. In fact, he had become famous in the world of advertising by creating the doctrine of "irrelevant revelations," a technique of responding to a difficult question or accusation by making a counteraccusation or raising a totally unrelated issue.

Dirk was emphatic that exigent circumstances required decisive action to restore Pop-Tarts to its rightful position as the category leader. The predicament they found themselves in was the fault of Human Resources' inability to recruit cutting-edge talent. All were in agreement until a junior product manager piped up with the observation that hadn't that same HR department recruited all of them? The comment was greeted with scorn and derision, coming from someone considered inexperienced and unfamiliar with the corporate managerial matrix.

It was then that Harold Hawking, who was married to the CEO's daughter and had the amorphous position of Senior Vice-President, Global Trends and Futuring, spoke up. Harold said he had been reading a glowing profile piece in the latest edition of *Bakery Confectionary News* about a young woman who had turned around the Twinkies brand. The article extolled her commitment to the company, their shared values, the responsibility of marketing to susceptible children, and the necessity to be forthright and candid with the consumer. The piece concluded with her advising those considering a career in corporate America to follow their passion, not the money, and counseled in so doing they would be fulfilled while making a contribution to a better world.

Clearly, she could be bought. Harold informed his

colleagues that in the bakery world, she was known as the madam of mendacity, an unscrupulous street fighter with an uncanny knack for self-promotion who ran roughshod over underlings or anyone who got in her way. Her name was Annika Svensson, and she was perfect for the Pop-Tarts job.

Russ Magpie liked what he was hearing and immediately contacted the head of HR and instructed her to make Annika Svensson an offer she couldn't refuse. It was to be loaded with stock options, double her current salary, and accompanied with assurances she would report directly to him and have unfettered use of the company plane. He then instructed the company's PR department to prepare a draft press release announcing that she was joining the company "after considerable soul searching" and concluding that "this position would allow her to continue to have a positive impact on the American family" while working for a company "dedicated to the key factors of ESG while embracing employee empowerment and world-class customer engagement and care."

CHAPTER 9

P. J. "Snakeboots" Jackson always got pumped at the advent of a new Congress. There were new members of Congress to be manipulated, new clients to be secured, maintained, and managed, new issues requiring novel approaches and remedies, and most importantly new money flowing into town. All this newness while he continued to enjoy the exclusivity of club life he cherished, Golf at Burning Tree, the exclusive men-only course (the members loved to chuckle that women were allowed in the pro shop at Christmastime to shop), lunch at the Metropolitan Club downtown with fellow movers and shakers, and another year in the Potomac Club, an invitation-only intimate dinner group of a dozen or so lobbyists that entertained members of the House and Senate for "off the record" gatherings. Club life was an integral aspect of being a power lobbyist, and P. J. was at the top of the influence-peddling pyramid.

Having your caricature on the wall of the Palm Restaurant in downtown DC was a clear indication you had made the big time. The Palm was a favorite watering hole for lobbyists and a place to see and be seen at lunch. Nothing was more ego-boosting and downright fun for Snakeboots than hosting clients or other lobbyists in his booth there, and this early January lobbyist gaggle was no different.

Lobbyists run in packs, like wolves. Agriculture/food lobbyists hang together, just like bank lobbyists are usually with other financial interests, and defense contractors are in the company of others feeding off the military-industrial complex. Snakeboots, as the premiere ag lobbyist, routinely ran with other so-called "foodies," since they attended the same fundraisers, dinners, and breakfasts, and worked with the same members on the same committees. It is a politically incestuous system of self-aggrandizement involving politicians, lobbyists, and special interests.

Joining him for lunch this day was Holly Hawkins, a spitfire lobbyist for the Consumer Brands Association (CBA), whose members made about everything you could buy in a grocery store; Charlie Harrison, head of government relations for the Food Marketing Institute (FMI), which represents the major grocery store chains in which Holly's members sold their products; and Randy Lesher of the American Farm Bureau (AFB), which grew all the crops and livestock to be made into food by the Consumer Brands and then sold by the members of FMI. Three characters most people had never heard of, yet they have great influence over what crops are grown and which livestock is raised, what food you eat, and how much it costs.

One given for every lobbyists lunch is that the bill will end up on the expense account of some trade association or client. Information gathering and networking grease the skids of the inside-the-beltway crowd and provide them the skinny on who is up, who is down, and what is the prevailing gossip. This info will then be used to scare the bejesus out of their members or clients, followed by an often-used warning: "If you don't have a seat at the table, you will be on the menu!" It doesn't matter that the so-called "facts" are often based only on speculation, conjecture, and rumors from "a reliable source" or "top Hill staffer"; they provide the grist for a call to arms. Using this "insider information," the affected interest will be warned that they better ramp up their presence or a major calamity will follow. If nothing happens, it was because of the presence and ingenuity of their DC office, and if something befalls the industry or company, obviously it requires beefing up their lobbying activity. A never-ending closed circle for an ever-growing lobby contingent in Washington.

The Holly, Charlie, Randy, and Snakeboots lunch followed a traditional pattern. Each lamented having to be back for another Congress that would be more acrimonious than ever before, segueing into complaining about how it was going to be difficult to get anything done, followed by the requisite stories of the old days of bipartisan goodwill. Revisionist history that is updated with each new Congress. Finally, after establishing the baseline on how difficult their jobs would be, they shifted to trading scuttlebutt about the newly elected members, especially Mickey Girtz of Florida, Lizzie Pendergast of Rhode Island, and Barb Breen of Georgia.

The consensus was they were all whack jobs. A leadership nightmare. Holly piped up that if Mikhail Gorbachev had seen these three buffoons before dismantling the Soviet Union, he would have reconsidered the whole democracy thing. Randy chimed in with the required phrase used by all farm lobbyists at least ten times per day when discussing members of Congress: "That dog won't hunt." Charlie summed it up by saying their only hope was for the leadership to provide some adult supervision for the three novice bedwetters.

Snakeboots was quiet as he mulled the conversation. Ever the mercenary, he finally joined in by commenting that he had three new clients and that he would figure out some way to take advantage of the three new loony bins on their behalf. He might use them on offense or defense, but either way, they might come in handy to get his clients the fair advantage they deserved. All his clients wanted was a level playing field tilted their way. He then summed up where they stood: "Gang, the agriculture approps bill is going to be north of $26 billion, which is enough slop to feed every special-interest pig in DC. We all know that it will become part of a massive omnibus spending package that will be passed in the middle of the night at the end of the session. It will be the legislative equivalent of linked sausage. The House will stuff their sausage, as will the Senate, and they will be linked together. During consideration and debate in the final passage, neither side will know or care what is in the other. All you need to do is get in one version or the other and you are home free. Forget all that civic book bull-shit about getting it through the House and Senate. One will do just fine. It is going to be a feeding frenzy, and I plan to get my fill."

CHAPTER 10

P. J. "Snakeboots" Jackson could talk a dog off a meat wagon. He was an unparalleled spin master and raconteur, with a good ol' boy image that beguiled both friend and foe. Beware, though, there was a reason his favorite snake boots were made from the skin of a copperhead, a snake known for its effective venom delivery system.

Competition for clients among DC lobby firms is cutthroat. Relationships ebb and flow as members of Congress come and go, with a seismic shift taking place every four or eight years with an incoming Presidential administration. Who you supported for election, when (money talks and early money shouts), and how much you contributed dictates access, which is the sine qua non of lobbyists. No access, no influence, no clients.

The walls of Snakeboots's K Street office were similar to those of every other lobbyist in town, adorned with pictures of him with notable politicians. The way he doled out campaign contributions, he could have a picture with just about anybody, and he did. Republicans, Democrats, liberals, and conservatives all graced his walls. A virtual rogues' gallery and a testament that he was no philosophy major, but simply a peddler of influence to be reckoned with. To him, politicians were simply tools in a toolbox to be used when required to get the job done.

Each new client brought challenges, and Rod McDonell

was no different. Snakeboots had posited some compelling arguments for the creation of a National Cricket Consortium when he and Rod were drinking Grasshoppers at the Entomological Society convocation. How much of that was just whiskey talk would need to be ferreted out at their first formal meeting in Washington.

Rod McDonell had never been to Washington, DC, before, and he was somewhat in awe as he peered out the airplane window during the river approach to Reagan National Airport. It was a panoramic view of the White House, Lincoln Memorial, Washington Monument, the National Mall, and the Capitol. He was a long way from his humble surroundings in North Georgia.

Appearances in the lobbying world are a critical aspect of client procurement, and having a car and driver is a fundamental component. Snakeboots had arranged for his man Trip Tanglewood to pick up Rod when he landed at Reagan National. Bedecked in the customary dark suit and skinny black tie, he would be outside baggage claim carrying a sign for Cricket Man.

Trip had two attributes that qualified him for the position of Snakeboots's wheelman. First and foremost, he was the wayward son of the congressman from North Dakota, Mark Tanglewood, who chaired the Subcommittee on Agricultural Appropriations. Representative Tanglewood and his wife were at wit's end when young Trip announced that he was quitting the University of North Dakota to take a gap year in order to find himself. He claimed that the fact that he had been arrested for public drunkenness and disorderly conduct for setting a couch on fire after the Fighting Hawks won the National Collegiate Hockey Championship did not impact his decision to take some time off to contemplate the future direction of his life. Seeing as he had bagged out of college and was now penniless, he landed in his parents' basement in Washington, DC.

Snakeboots, who was a firm believer in giving someone a second chance, hired Trip sight unseen after the congressman's chief of staff mentioned at a fundraiser that Mr. and Mrs. Tanglewood would be forever indebted to anyone willing to give Trip a gig so he would leave the house once and for all. The fact that the congressman had control over the $26 billion budget of the Department of Agriculture had no bearing on the lobbyist's decision to hire the young man.

The other attribute Trip possessed was that he was a human sieve. Whether it was tidbits picked up at the family dinner table about the Ag Appropriations' inner workings or a client conversation from the back of the car, Trip would capture information and reliably report every detail and nuance to Snakeboots.

After being picked up at the airport, Rod thought it was pretty cool to be riding in the back of a Lincoln Town Car with the latest editions of the *Washington Post*, *New York Times*, *Wall Street Journal*, and *Roll Call*—the Capitol Hill newspaper. He had to call somebody, so he called his parents in Ellijay, Georgia, to let them know he was in high cotton. They needed to know their boy had hit the big time. Trip had overheard similar conversations every time a new client first arrived from the provinces.

Rod was escorted into Snakeboots's office by Ruby, his admin, who like everyone else in the office had done a stint on Capitol Hill. Ruby, in her younger days, after winning the Miss Baton Twirling contest in Johnson County, Texas, was hired by the local congressman Charlie "Good Time" Jones, whose outer office looked like a recovery room for Las Vegas call girls. Congressman Jones served numerous terms but was finally defeated when his lifestyle collided with his evangelical constituency. Ruby and the rest of the outer office team easily found positions on other congressional staff or downtown, since they were known to have information regarding the most intimate details of Capitol Hill. In other words, Ruby and the other ladies knew a lot.

Snakeboots had a shtick he would go into when a new client first entered his office. He would excuse himself and ask Ruby to make a call to Senator So-and-So. Ruby then would announce Senator So-and-So was on the line, which he would then pick up and bellow out, "Senator, Snakeboots here" and then carry on a one-sided animated conversation. Harking out statements like, "Glad to work with you on that," "No problem," "You can count on me," and "Looking forward to getting together." On the other end of the line was a totally befuddled, lowly Hill staffer with no idea who this man was or what he was talking about. The client, listening to the Snakeboots side of the conversation, would be quite impressed with him talking directly to the senator. The lowly staffer assigned to answer the office phone would usually report to the office manager that he had received another crank call.

Rod's head was swirling. Damn, this guy could just call up and talk to senators. He knew he had the right man in Snakeboots, but he had two nagging concerns. How would he be able to pay Snakeboots's fees, and if he did manage to pay the freight, exactly how would they get funding for the consortium? Best, he thought, to be direct with Snakeboots.

"I don't have the bucks to pay you, and if I did, just how the hell do we get the dough?"

As you might expect, our esteemed lobbyist did not miss a beat on either point. The place to park and receive the funds would be the Department of Agriculture's Rural Development program. It was the basket of boondoggles in the Department of Agriculture. A mere $5 million to create a National Cricket Consortium would barely cause a ripple with all the other money sloshing around in that program. Once funded and created, the consortium would contract with Rod McDonell, the famous Cricket Man, to be the Executive Director at a compensation level sufficient to entice him to leave professional fishing and start a new career in public service for the betterment of agriculture and rural America.

Now as far as Snakeboots's take on all of this, he knew that it was illegal to charge a commission or take a contingency based on lobbying for funding, so he would mount this lobbying effort gratis for the public good. However, once Rod was the Executive Director, he would retain the law firm of Snakeboots Jackson for a few hundred thousand dollars per year, allowing Snakeboots to lobby for additional appropriations for the consortium down the road. An arrangement that would translate into a lucrative legislative-funded perpetual motion machine for the firm and Cricket Man.

Having dispatched with all those pesky details regarding funding and compensation, Snakeboots suggested it was time for lunch at the Palm. Questions concerning timing, strategy, and the like they could work out later, plus he had to get moving since he had another new client meeting that afternoon.

CHAPTER 11

Meetings of the American Society of Association Executives (ASAE) are usually convivial affairs, albeit with a slight mosh pit aspect to them. To start with, everybody knows the organization should be called the Association of Association Executives, but the snicker factor with that name is just too high, so substituting American Society works just fine.

Convivial is not hard to understand, considering the 48,000 members from 7,400 disparate organizations are mostly glad-handing extroverts, a personality required of trade association types. The mosh pit component comes from the competition among trade associations fighting for limited corporate membership dollars. It is a matter of survival.

Clyde Cartwright, Executive Director of the National Hot Dog and Sausage Council, had gleaned a lot of helpful advice and information from the ASAE meetings and convocations over the years. Simple but useful suggestions, like setting up a website chock-full of claptrap and gaseous minutiae that the media could use as filler. The council website now designated "Hot Dog Ambassadors," which usually created a local press blurb about where the new ambassador lived. It also provided useless but fun facts, such as twenty billion hot dogs are consumed in the US each year, which equates to approximately seventy per person. Also, amazingly, it informed you that Mickey Mouse's first words when movies went from silent to talkies were "hot dog." These factoids and others were a treasure trove for reporters looking for trivia and helped promote the consumption of more hot dogs and sausages.

There are a lot of sharp elbows thrown in the trade association world under the guise of congeniality. Companies annually review what associations to join, maintain, or discontinue. It is the "What have you done lately for me?" evaluation. A process that had Clyde disheartened as he left the ASAE annual meeting in early January, realizing his board was once again going to ask why was there no official hot dog month or day like the ice cream guys had.

July is National Ice Cream Month, and the third Sunday in July is National Ice Cream Day. Now, there are a lot of national this and that days and months, but they are self-declared and self-promoted by the particular industry, e.g., National Peanut Brittle Day. Ice cream, however, under the auspices of their trade association, the International Dairy Foods Association (IDFA), pulled off a PR coup. Way back in 1984, they somehow convinced President Ronald Reagan to issue Presidential Proclamation 5219, which stated:

> Now, Therefore, I, Ronald Reagan, President of the United States of America, do hereby proclaim July 1984 as National Ice Cream Month and July 15, 1984, as National Ice Cream Day, and I call upon the people of the United States to observe these events with appropriate ceremonies and activities.

In Witness Whereof, I have hereunto set my hand this ninth day of July, in the year of the Lord nineteen hundred and eighty-four, and of the Independence of the United States of America the two hundred and ninth.

Ronald Reagan

In addition to the Presidential Proclamation, they were also able to gin up passage of Senate Joint Resolution 298, which called for the country to recognize a month and day dedicated to eating ice cream. They effectively had the entire federal government telling people to pound down a product that every nutritionist would tell you to go easy on. The Presidential Proclamation and Senate Joint Resolution should have been called the Lobbyist Enrichment Act of 1984. Every food trade association executive and hired-gun lobbyist considered this the gold standard of industry self-promotion. One could only imagine the bonuses the leadership of the International Dairy Foods Association received, not to mention the length of the contract extensions for executives who had helped pull this off.

It always piqued Clyde that IDFA was able to accomplish what it did, and it especially burned his ass when some of his members would be invited to attend the annual ice cream social on Capitol Hill to commemorate their national month. Invariably they would come back saying, "Why don't we have a day or month like that?" Implicit in the question was a suggestion that maybe he wasn't up to the job. It was putting pressure on Clyde to get official recognition of hot dogs and sausages, and he knew this was the year to put on the full-court press or get his resume ready and start looking for a new job. To get this done, however, he knew would need reinforcements, so he scheduled a meeting with the top lobbyist gunslinger in town—P. J. "Snakeboots" Jackson.

Snakeboots returned to the office in a great mood after lunch with the Cricket Man. Several members of Congress had stopped by his booth at the Palm to fawn over him and exclaim his lobbying prowess in front of his new client. The fawning and the exclaiming are all part of the DC dance ritual. Members of Congress need lobbyists to donate to their campaigns. Lobbyists need clients in order to afford to donate to congressional campaigns. This symbiotic relationship results in a mating dance that goes on hundreds of times a day in Washington, DC. It goes like this: When a congressperson runs into a lobbyist with a client, they immediately heap praise on the lobbyist as the most influential, persuasive, and impactful lobbyist they know, thereby indirectly praising the client for having the smarts to hire him or her. The member then asks the client what brought them to Washington, to which they react, while feigning deep interest and concern, by asking the lobbyist what needs to be done. The lobbyist then responds using what is called "inside the beltway lingo," referencing committees, jurisdiction, chairmen, the legislative calendar, and other extraneous factoids so he can demonstrate he has special knowledge and expertise. The encounter concludes, regardless of the answer or whether the congressperson has a clue what they are talking about, with the honorable member offering, "Let me know how I can help."

Clyde Cartwright, Executive Director of the National Hot Dog and Sausage Council, spent his time waiting for Snakeboots looking at all the political pictures that adorned the walls of his office. It was an impressive display; in fact, it was the best display money could buy. When Snakeboots arrived, he apologized for his tardiness and asked that Clyde bear with him as he had to make one quick call, but no need for him to leave the office. Just make himself comfortable on the couch. He then yelled out for Ruby to get Senator Staubitz, chair of the Senate Agriculture Committee, on the phone.

"Hello, senator. Snakeboots here. Glad I could be of help. Yep, yep, you are so right. I couldn't agree more." He then went on to question the timing of the introduction of the agriculture appropriations bill, while on the other end of the line, a totally befuddled intern who was answering the phones was speechless. Finally, Snakeboots concluded with, "Yes, senator, that's right, I will be glad to work with you on that project. Feel free to call me anytime."

When he hung up, the flummoxed intern reported to the office manager that he had received an indecipherable call from a delusional constituent who spoke with him as if he were the senator. The manager advised him there was no reason to be concerned: "This town is filled with plenty of nuts and kooks, but most of them are harmless."

Clyde now had Snakeboots's undivided attention and launched right into what his problem was and how he needed help. He explained how he felt his job was on the line unless he could create something that compared with the National Ice Cream Month/Day. He needed some political splash and was ready to put Snakeboots on a hefty twelve-month retainer if he was willing and able to take on the job.

Snakeboots, as he was wont to do, gave his best look of deep-felt empathy, concern, and interest, then cautioned Clyde that this would be a very difficult and hence expensive undertaking. He counseled that the Senate had soured on national day/month designations, so they would need to look to the House, which was just now being organized, to establish a legislative foothold. There they had two options to consider. Both would require a frontal attack with D-Day-like precision. The agriculture authorization bill, which creates departments and programs, was up for renewal, and of course, the agriculture appropriations bill, which was expected to be introduced to the tune of $26 billion and would have a plethora of nooks and crannies that could be stuffed with special interest provisions, chicanery, and mischief. Not that what they were proposing would constitute a special interest, chicanery, or mischief, but even the noblest of causes can be misconstrued.

"I think we go with the approps bill," advised Snakeboots. "More cover in that massive spending bill. We simply put in a rider directing the Department of Agriculture to spend X dollars to designate a month or day in honor of hot dogs. No one will see it coming until it is a done deal."

Clyde liked what he was hearing and especially the war metaphor of possibly attacking on two fronts, but then narrowing the field of battle to the ag approps bill. Those terms would excite his board of directors and, even if they were unsuccessful, buy him another year as Executive Director. Victory, he would argue, was just around the corner.

Snakeboots agreed to the terms of the retainer and

suggested they go to the Monocle restaurant on Capitol Hill for drinks to celebrate their new business relationship. The Monocle was a favorite watering hole for politicians of all stripes and a place where elected officials would fawn over Snakeboots, praise Clyde for retaining Snakeboots, and offer to help "in any way they can." A celebration made all the sweeter now that it was all expensable to the National Hot Dog and Sausage Council.

CHAPTER 12

Wall Street applauded the announcement of Annika Svensson joining Kellogg Company as Senior Vice-President of Nutrition Marketing, Family Values, and Customer Welfare. A title that won plaudits on the woke scale as encompassing everything while meaning nothing. This position crowned Annika the queen of Pop-Tarts, Cheez-Its, Rice Krispie Treats, and health bars. The financial community loved the fact that she was "as cuddly as a porcupine" and had a "pit bull demeanor," guaranteeing a cultural tsunami in the staid halls of Kellogg.

Annika was a take-charge person. On her first day as Senior Vice-President, she heard that Dirk Dantley of Gray Fog, Inc., who managed the Pop-Tart advertising account, was at home with his wife relishing time with their first newborn. She placed a call to him to extend her warmest congratulations but also to let him know that unless there was a rapid and dramatic increase in Pop-Tart sales, he was toast. When Dirk protested, since he had only been on the Pop-Tart account for a month, it only raised her ire, causing her to blurt out that as Vice-President of Family Values, she could arrange for him to be available to spend a lot of time with his family.

Her next call was to Barrett Childress, the company's general counsel, to get an update on the class-action lawsuit and the burgeoning so-called "Pop-Tart Reform

Movement." This activity trending on social media was causing consternation among young mothers, whose allegations were based on nonsensical, negative nutritional notions that Pop-Tarts didn't contain enough fruit to make claims on the label. This movement among the food police was dangerously close to spiraling out of control and now was expanding to include charges that Cheez-Its were not made with real cheese. If only consumers would pay attention to the Cheez-It commercials on college football days, they would know that this line of attack was unfounded!

Annika considered Barrett Childress a corporate soulmate with his tunnel-vision approach and general disdain for the consuming public. She could identify with his "people have to learn how to take a joke" response to the class-action lawsuit and his "squash them like a bug" approach to any challenge from the reform movement. Being an expert corporate infighter, she called for an off-site meeting with the general counsel, chief ethics officer, Vice-President of Public Affairs, and the newly appointed person identified as social media warlord to develop a synergistic, unified approach to eliminating the lawsuit and annihilating the Pop-Tart Reform Movement. It was time to demonstrate her corporate mettle. They were under attack.

She began the meeting by drawing a battleship on the whiteboard in front of the assembled group, whom she now referred to as "fellow combatants." She likened the battleship to the company, i.e., Battleship *Kellogg*, and reminded everyone that a battleship is designed to take hits while continuing to fight. The incoming torpedoes of the class-action lawsuit and the Pop-Tart Reform Movement were no match for the ship's heavy armor and big guns when trained on the enemy. It was their sworn duty on behalf of the stock-holders and the executive bonus program to turn the force and might of Battleship *Kellogg* on those who would assault what was sacrosanct. She then put up pictures of President Zelensky and Winston Churchill as role models of leadership in trying times. The situation called for a counteroffensive, and they were the ones to lead the attack.

The speech and the battleship metaphor riled the group into a frenzy. The chief ethics officers announced that they needed to mount a no-holds-barred campaign, and the general counsel chimed in that cost would be no object. The social media warlord offered to mount a disinformation campaign that would imply that Russian hackers were spreading lies on the web about Pop-Tarts, and the Vice-President of Public Affairs pronounced he would lead by following. Annika had created total unanimity without anyone having a clue but her as to how they would accomplish any of this.

In a sidebar with Counsel Childress, she puffed him up as having a brilliant legal mind when he pledged that cost was no object. What they needed, according to Annika, was a settlement with a nondisclosure agreement with the plaintiffs' law firm. The firm's phone number—1-800-Get-Cash—was a constant presence on late-night TV and billboards, so it was obvious it was all about the Benjamins, i.e., money. Making a deal with them was the legal equivalent of dragging a dollar bill through a trailer park. Dangle enough moola in front of them, and they would quietly go away, and the ambulance chasers would focus on the next sacrificial lamb.

Following up with the social media warlord, it was

agreed that somehow they would plant the seeds that the movement was tangentially tied to the Benghazi hearings, Hunter Biden's laptop, and the Steele dossier. Since nobody really remembered or understood what any of that was about, it would cause enough sinister overtones to discredit any information or facts promulgated by members of the movement as simply the ruminations of anti-American malcontents.

Finally, in the wrap-up session after lunch, Annika announced to the group that it was the design of a battleship to go on the offensive and that she had been developing the mother of all counteroffensives in the world of food marketing. She had instructed the Gray Fog, Inc. advertising agency to develop a long-term ad campaign that would position Pop-Tarts as a health food. To augment the media campaign, she authorized a seven-figure grant to the Artificial Ingredient Institute at the University of Buffalo to study and document how artificial ingredients increase SAT and ACT scores in high school students. She also was making a $750,000 contribution to the Food Marketing program at Western Michigan University to study how Pop-Tart sales coincided with increased sales of orange juice and milk. The ad campaign and the studies were Battleship *Kellogg* weapons to ready the turf for the big invasion. Sort of like the big guns pounding the beaches of Normandy. The actual invasion would result in Pop-Tarts becoming part of the USDA School Breakfast program. She then disclosed that she'd had a clandestine meeting with the powerful lobbyist P. J. "Snakeboots" Jackson. She had witnessed firsthand his access and influence. When she was in his office, he'd called and spoken directly with Senator Sally

Staubitz, chair of the Senate Agriculture Committee. She had witnessed how politically connected he was at lunch when numerous members of Congress came to their table, and everyone stated, "Let me know how I can help." He was a force to be reckoned with and the man for the job.

She and Snakeboots had hatched a plan that if successful would be a game-changer for Pop-Tarts. All of their careers and bonuses would be golden. In order for this to succeed, however, she needed buy-in from everyone. The idea was genius in its simplicity and humongous in its impact on the bottom line. It would take no additional marketing dollars, no additional promotional activity, and involve no additional overhead costs. All they had to do was get Pop-Tarts included as an eligible item in the School Breakfast program, and sales would soar.

The group was quiet. No one had anticipated this, and no one wanted to be the naysayer. They would all win if successful, and they could point the finger at her if it went to hell in a handbasket. No time for profiles in courage. The consensus was to go for it, and this was summed up by the Vice-President of Public Affairs, who unequivocally stated, "I will follow."

CHAPTER 13

In lobbyist lingo, you need a horse. Someone you can ride. A member of Congress who will introduce a bill or amendment to legislation and will call in some chits to make it happen. Oftentimes, introducing or co-sponsoring a provision is merely cosmetic and a way to ingratiate themselves with an interest group. This is especially true if they express that their involvement is based on "deep concern" or "dismay," which translates into they will do nothing. What you need is someone who will really work on the issue.

Picking the right horse is the key to successful lobbying. Typically, a winning horse is on the relevant committee or subcommittee and a member of the majority party. There are, however, factors that may weigh against this common axiom. Does he or she play ball? The legendary former Speaker of the House Sam Rayburn would advise new members of Congress, "To get along—go along," which meant, in legislative parlance, to be there when the leadership needed them. If they went along when needed, the leadership would reciprocate when a member really wanted something.

Another element to be weighed when picking a horse is how important the issue will be politically when they are up for re-election. This factor will influence how hard they will work. Getting re-elected is the ultimate motivating aspect in activating a congressional office and in passing legislation. Nothing else even compares.

Finally, one other angle that's often overlooked when deciding who to ride: Who are their friends and foes? Just because they are a Democrat, Republican, liberal, or conservative, a savvy lobbyist will understand that there may be intangibles that are not readily apparent. Snakeboots had a knack for understanding the dynamics of member-to-member relationships. He was an insider looking out as opposed to an outsider looking in.

The official title is the Appropriations Subcommittee on Agriculture, Rural Development, Food and Drug Administration, and Other Related Agencies. The chair of the subcommittee, Mark Tanglewood (R-ND), and everyone else just called it the Ag Approps. It had a total of fourteen members, of which nine were Republicans and five were Democrats. A back-scratching collection of rogue representatives whose primary concern was sending pork back to their home districts and getting re-elected.

Now, at first blush, you would assume it would be a smart bet to ride a majority member of the subcommittee. Snakeboots, however, had some insider intelligence that led him to approach Representative Lucy Sprout, a freshman Democrat from California, to pursue funding for the National Cricket Consortium.

Congresswoman Sprout was considered one of the five freshman fabulists, a loosely defined group of new representatives whose credentials, at least those they'd claimed while campaigning, stretched credulity. None of them allowed the truth to get in the way. Although Lucy could not compare to their de facto leader George Sandoz, who had created an entirely fictional persona out of whole cloth, she did perpetuate a pretty good myth.

Lucy's yarn, while not as extensive and elaborate as Sandoz's, was highly effective for advancement and recognition with cause-conscious Progressive Democrats. Ever since she had played the role of Pocahontas in her third-grade play, she had claimed to be part Native American and a member of the Powhatan Tribe, a designation that allowed her to benefit as a diversity candidate when seeking admission to elite schools and colleges. She also used it in the campaign to claim her election would be historical, in that she would be the first indigenous person to represent her district in Congress, and that would be further proof that her constituents were not inherently racist. The fact that she had blonde hair and blue eyes and the name Sprout was an Ellis Island derivative of the Dutch name *Sprute* somehow was lost on her Republican opponent and the voters.

More important than her ability to lie, however, was that, according to Trip Tanglewood, the chairman's son and Snakeboots's driver, Congresswoman Sprout had hired the chairman's niece as her special assistant for Constituent Outreach. The niece had been pursuing a degree in cannabis cultivation at People University but flunked out. Her therapist described her as "lethargic, unfocused, and in a continual state of brain fog," a condition that did not deter the congresswoman from hiring the niece for a no-show job. She told her chief of staff the young woman could re-energize, refocus, and concentrate on her cannabis-related academic pursuits. Congresswoman Sprout defended the hire by describing the young woman as "uniquely genetically qualified."

In addition, Representative Sprout had one other extremely positive attribute in that she was in a very public and visceral spat with Republican freshman Barb Breen of Georgia. Chairman Tanglewood detested Congresswoman Breen, as did most other members, and would do about anything to help any political enemy of the lady from Georgia.

Representative Breen, shortly after being sworn in, had attacked Chairman Tanglewood as a "boot-licking lackey" of Speaker McCrudy and stalwart of his "gazpacho tactics." All this was a result of the chairman's refusal to support funding for an anti-drone missile system within the USDA to shoot down the climate activists' lasers that the congresswoman claimed were causing forest fires in her district. Her malapropism of substituting "gazpacho" for "Gestapo" caused a precipitous drop in the stock of Campbell Soup, and tomato future prices collapsed. Campbell, in an attempt to mitigate the damage, took out a full-page ad in the *Wall Street Journal* emphatically pronouncing that they did not sell soup in Germany from 1939 to 1945. The International Fresh Produce Association, trying to avert a further drop in the price of tomatoes, issued a report declaring that it was anticipated that cold soup sales, especially gazpacho, would quadruple in the next few years, due to climate change.

The flap over gazpacho and tomatoes hit Congresswoman Sprout's rural agricultural district quite hard. The central California region she represented was a major provider of tomatoes for the nation, and the brouhaha was causing a significant economic hit on her corporate farmers, who were also her biggest contributors. They were not happy and demanded she do something.

Congresswoman Sprout, with the encouragement of

Speaker McCrudy and Chairman Tanglewood, launched a counterattack. Decrying the lack of civility and comity in Washington, she called Congresswoman Breen a "mindless bloviator" and a "fringe, unstable megalomaniac" who should immediately apologize to the "gazpacho lovers of this great nation" and tomato growers everywhere.

Snakeboots sensed a wide opening for his client with the public rift between the two freshmen. As a favorite of Speaker McCrudy and Chairman Tanglewood, anything Congresswoman Sprout wanted was hers for the asking. There was no cricket connection between her and her district and no cricket contributions to raise the ire of the irritating, snoopy press. Introducing legislation to create a National Cricket Consortium would position her as an agricultural stateswoman working on behalf of the country as a whole. It was also an opportunity for the congresswoman to secure a commitment from the Speaker that she would not encounter any serious Republican opponent in the next election, while at the same time opening fundraising opportunities in the cricket industry. Another plus was that the creation of the consortium might provide a place to offload Chairman Tanglewood's niece if the legislation was successful.

The press conference to announce the introduction of H.R. 1776, the National Cricket Consortium Act of 2023, was held in the foyer of the Cannon House Office Building. Congresswoman Lucy Sprout (D-CA) was the principal sponsor with two co-sponsors. Congressman Buzz Orkin (D-AZ), an heir to the Orkin Pest Control fortune, who thought his co-sponsorship might be a salve for the millions of insects his family had exterminated, and Congressman Raji Nehru (R-NY), who was of Indian descent and whose

staff had mistakenly thought the consortium was to promote the game of cricket, which was a favorite of the
congressman.

Joining the three esteemed members of Congress at
the press conference were the usual trade associations and
interest groups. The Entomological Society of America,
the National Pest Control Management Association, the
National Fishing Association, and the North American
Coalition for Insect Agriculture all attended and were
joined, for no apparent reason, by the Association of
Tomato Growers and the Gazpacho Lovers of America
Club, escorted by the lobbyist for Campbell Soup.

All gathered trumpeted the benefits of cricket farms
to the national economy and the consumption of crickets
to the nutritional health of the nation. They went on to
explain how the passage of this bipartisan legislation would
create thousands of high-paying jobs in rural communities
in construction, transportation, cricket maintenance, bug
research, marketing, and sales. A ripple effect would also
be felt in increased sales of fishing rods, boats, canoes, and
fishing garb. Tangentially, this projected multiplier impact
resulted in Charles Schwab issuing a buy recommendation
on Orvis stock and a 22% increase in their share price. A
jump in price later became the subject of a Department of
Justice investigation into insider trading when it became
known that six members of Congress had bought the stock
the night before the press conference.

Introduced with great fanfare, all the insiders knew the
bill would never be enacted into law. It was a Trojan horse
to draw attention to the cricket industry while they quietly
slipped funding into the behemoth ag appropriations bill, a

deceptive sleight of hand routinely performed by that master legislative prestidigitator Snakeboots Jackson, a bait and switch in the halls of Congress.

CHAPTER 14

Manipulating the media is part and parcel of any lobby undertaking. The cable networks require a never-ending stream of blather and are always on the lookout for controversy. Especially appetizing is a flap between political clowns on the left and the right. A smart lobbyist will feed a story to sympathetic reporters, provide some spin, and hope it gets traction. Negative is okay so long as it is directed at the right member of Congress who, as the target, may galvanize the opposition while motivating your supporters.

Lizzie Pendergast (D-RI) was generally considered by her colleagues to be a royal pain in the ass. Sanctimonious beyond all get out, she was oblivious to the fact that not all members of Congress were of the manor born and thought that tofu was a staple of everyone's diet. Political considerations had no impact when they collided with her philosophical leanings. One time she went so far as to call a fellow Democrat a "misogynist barbarian" when he wouldn't agree to sign a letter to the Department of Transportation demanding that they cease using the term "manhole" and begin calling it a "person hole." It's not hard to imagine what kind of "hole" he called her. It was her "my way or the highway" approach to public policy that made her a darling of the far-left libs and the scourge of the right-wing, flat-earth troops. If you ever wanted someone to attack your client and your cause, it was her.

Clyde Cartwright had reported to his board that he was going to initiate a full-court press to receive official recognition of National Hot Dog Day. He used every cliché, including that it was going to be "all hands on deck," a "battle royal," and a "fight to the finish," and that he had retained the services of the "Big Dog" in town, Snakeboots Jackson. He recounted how, the other day at lunch with Snakeboots, numerous members of Congress had already offered to "help in any way they can." He briefed the board on how they could attack on two fronts. Both the Ag Authorization and the Ag Approps were possibilities, but Ag Approps was the way to go. It would be a no-holds-barred concerted effort, and support of National Hot Dog Day would be the sole criteria for financial support and an endorsement in the next election. It was going to be black or white. You were either for us or against us. There was going to be no middle ground or waffling. This was war.

Clyde's stirring presentation caused his board to stand with applause. They were committed, and Clyde imagined himself the General Patton of DC trade associations. Now on to battle.

The first strategy session between Clyde and Snakeboots took place at the Palm in the booth under the caricature of the legendary lobbyist. Having a retainer arrangement also meant another place to park expensable items, like the lunch they were having. Despite the Pattonesque presentation Clyde had made to his board, Snakeboots suggested they exercise caution and not over-promise. Both the House and the Senate frowned on making any new designations. Just the other day, he cautioned, the House had rejected making the first Tuesday of October National Pork Rind Day as part of the Childhood Anti-Obesity Legislation. Hard to believe, but true. Creating a National Hot Dog Day would be tough sledding and require a unique approach.

Never at a loss, Snakeboots had a plan up his sleeve. They would mount the lobby equivalent of a false flag operation. It would put the leadership of the Progressive caucus in a dither, thereby inciting Fox News, OAN, Truth Social, and the rest of the regressive right into attack mode. Once the right-wing media was frothing at the mouth with claims that the anti-hot-dog zealots were simply political arsonists attacking the American way of life, the lefties would have to counterattack. CNN would form a panel of twenty-six scholars to discuss the philosophical underpinnings of national day designations. MSNBC would elucidate on how the rally Snakeboots envisioned differed from the J6 Riot at the Capitol and how it really was just a normal visit by tourists. One could even imagine the *New York Times* editorializing the need for a select committee to be formed to investigate the origins of the rally and whether it had any connection to QAnon.

Once the media manipulation was underway, the momentum would shift politically from "if something should be done" to "what should be done." Politicians love to fix problems where none exist, and once something is done, it is sort of like the end of the Vietnam War—they just declare victory and go home. The false flag operation envisioned by Snakeboots would be a showstopper. The plan was to simply stage a rally on the Capitol grounds in honor of the all-American hot dog, as if it had received official recognition. Free hot dogs for members of Congress, their staff, and their families. Since everybody loves a pet show, they would invite the Dachshund Breeders of America to participate and bring their dogs. In addition, so sausage makers didn't feel left out, they would have a Jimmy Dean impersonator provide the entertainment. It would be a bipartisan, gala event wrapped in red, white, and blue. Everybody would love it except the one person you didn't want to—Congresswoman Lizzie Pendergast (D-RI).

Her opposition will sway every undecided vote our way, calculated Snakeboots's Machiavellian mind. If she opposed it, then it must have some merit would be the thinking of the right and the rational middle, and there was no doubt she would be outraged over the rally and the notion of a National Hot Dog Day. It would be an opportunity for her as the lead contrarian to get in front of a camera, which is what she lived for. She would be encouraged to do so by her senior legislative assistant, who before working for her had chaired NETA (Never Eat the Animal), a division of People for the Ethical Treatment of Animals (PETA). The aide had attained this vaunted position in the world of veganism as a result of her activity as a field organizer for the Animal Justice Party, where she received notoriety and acclaim for organizing the burning of Colonel Sanders in effigy, causing an entire Kentucky Fried Chicken restaurant to be torched.

Clyde was ecstatic with what he was hearing. This would blow his membership away. An event like this would make what the International Dairy Foods Association did for ice cream look like a sideshow. However, there was one element he wanted to add that would assure their rally was the crème de la crème of DC events and make his biggest member very happy. How about they have the Wienermobile make an appearance? He could arrange for the best two hot doggers, aka drivers, who drove under the pseudonyms Molly Mustard and Peter Pork to be at the wheel. No downside and a guaranteed crowd-pleaser. Everyone would want their picture taken with the famous American icon. This would be an event long remembered in Washington.

Snakeboots and Clyde had a plan. Time to celebrate with another round of expensable drinks.

CHAPTER 15

Representative Mickey Girtz (R-FL) was an A#1 aeolist. He actually believed his own press clippings, and even though he was a freshman member of Congress, he looked in the mirror every day and saw a future senator or maybe even a president. He was realistic enough, however, to realize that in order to fulfill these delusional aspirations, he would need to manufacture some bona fides where none existed. Especially in the military and defense sectors. A daunting task for someone with absolutely no military knowledge or background, but made plausible by the election of fabulist five serial fraudster George Sandoz. Here was a guy who created an entire career in finance and banking while running for office in the backyard of the greatest financial institutions in the world, and no one was the wiser. His success made Mickey feel like a laggard in the burgeoning field of campaign creationism, where if you unflinchingly told the lie enough times it became the truth. It was a tactical area in which he knew he could excel with a little bit of practice.

His congressional district in the Florida Panhandle had a significant military presence and a slew of retired military snowbirds. During the campaign, he had successfully neutralized his lack of military service by claiming he had earned his stripes through his patriotic mastering of *Call of Duty*, a reference that confounded his septuagenarian and octogenarian constituents, who had no idea it was a video game. Realizing this deflection might work during a congressional campaign, he understood it probably wouldn't pass muster if he sought a higher office. He needed to stake out a presence in defense-related matters. He needed to initiate legislation that would identify him as a critical thinker and a military strategist. The legislation would secure him coverage on shows as disparate as *The View*, *The Five*, and maybe even the Steve Bannon podcast *War Room*. If successful, he would be recognized as an expert because he was called an expert. Kind of like the Kardashians and Paris Hilton—famous because they are famous. An image created out of thin air.

Eureka! It came to him while watching a documentary on the History Channel that was trying to demystify the late Secretary of Defense Donald Rumsfeld's most famous quote. Secretary Rumsfeld had famously extrapolated on his decision-making when he said, "There are known knowns—there are many things we know we know," and then went on to say, "We also know there are some things we do not know. But there are also unknown unknowns, the ones we don't know we don't know."

The documentary credited the secretary as being the overlord of obfuscation with this totally impenetrable statement. It then went on to report that while he was Secretary of Defense during the Afghanistan War, Rumsfeld had ordered the US military to drop 2.4 million Pop-Tarts to feed the population of the country, while admittedly not knowing if the citizens of Afghanistan would eat Pop-Tarts. The documentary then went on to disclose that Secretary Rumsfeld had served on the Kellogg board and obviously knew things unknown to others about the strategic significance of Pop-Tarts in military tactics. After seeing and hearing all of this, Mickey now knew what he had not known and began drafting legislation.

Nothing in DC is quite as terrifying as when a legislator drafts legislation without the direction or guidance of a lobbyist. Some members of Congress actually think that it is what they were sent there to do. In this situation, Mickey Girtz didn't know what he didn't know, but that had never stopped him in the past and it wouldn't now. He planned to require Pop-Tarts as part of meals-ready-to-eat (MRE) for the armed services. He was convinced this was both politically and militarily brilliant. A dangerous notion, since the word *brilliant* had never appeared in the same sentence as Mickey's name.

His thinking was the soldiers, sailors, and airmen would love him for replacing the bland components of existing MREs with fun, tasty Pop-Tarts. Sure, some nagging nutritionists might try to raise a ruckus, but what did they know? They had never been elected to anything. He could cite no less an authority than Donald Rumsfeld who as secretary of defense must have known what he was doing when he dropped them into Afghanistan. If they were good enough for Afghanistan, they were good enough for our troops, reasoned the congressman. Not only could they be used for sustenance, but they could also be something to barter if ever a service member was captured in combat. Who wouldn't trade a bowl of rice for a Pop-Tart?

In addition, introducing Pop-Tart legislation would make him a social media sensation and the darling of two critical constituencies. First, the hundred million-strong fans of Justin Bieber, known as Beliebers, were all aware of their star's affinity for Pop-Tarts, which would cause them to swoon over the congressman. It might even create an opportunity for a photo op of him with Justin on stage when the singer was getting ready to down a Pop-Tart, as he was known to do.

The other constituency would be the millions of fans of Jerry Seinfeld. Sources in Hollywood had made Mickey aware that Seinfeld was soon to release a Netflix documentary on the history of Pop-Tarts. Mickey figured as the author of national Pop-Tart legislation, it would be difficult not to invite him to the awards ceremony, and he had visions of walking down the red carpet under the glare of the paparazzi. He would be vaulted from relative political obscurity to a household name as Jerry's main man.

Congressman Girtz was pumped. The introduction of his first piece of legislation was going to be accompanied by all sorts of pomp and circumstance deserving of this august occasion. He reserved the foyer of the Cannon House Office Building, following the congresswoman from California Lucy Sprout, who was also introducing her first bill—something to do with crickets. The juxtaposition of the two press conferences appealed to Mickey and made him feel like a statesman. He was addressing a grave matter of national defense, and she was babbling on about some parochial matter concerning bugs.

Sixteen American flags formed a semicircle in the foyer of the Cannon Building and served as a backdrop to a podium bearing the seal of the State of Florida. The Florida State University ROTC bugle corps was playing "Charge" as the congressman and his entourage filed in. He was accompanied by the quartermaster of Pensacola VFW Post

706, the commander of Tallahassee American Legion Post 13, the President of the Tallahassee Beliebers Fan Club, and two students with signs bearing the face of *Seinfeld*'s George Costanza. Congressman Girtz stood solemnly behind the podium, basking in the lights of the TV networks and the shutter clicks of cameras. To him, this was when he would demonstrate he was the man for the moment. His remarks would identify him as a student of history and someone to be reckoned with in matters of national security.

"It is with humility that I stand before you today to introduce the Donald Rumsfeld Pop-Tarts National Preparedness Act of 2023. Not since the Know-Nothing Party of the 1850s has knowledge been so important. Sure, there are many unknowns, but knowing what I know, I knew it was time for decisive action. This legislation will let members of the armed forces know that we care about them and put our enemies on notice, knowing what they will confront if, knowingly or unknowingly, they put our brave warriors in harm's way. This will let the world know we stand behind those who fight for our freedom."

The Kellogg company switchboard lit up like the sky on the Fourth of July. Media, consumer groups, veteran organizations, you name it, all wanted a reaction to the big news out of Washington that Pop-Tarts might become a staple in MREs for the military. The poor switchboard operator was in a panic. The company media relations group knew nothing about it, nor did public affairs. The military sales team didn't know what they were talking about, and the Pop-Tart brand managers didn't have a clue what was going on. Finally, the CEO's administrative assistant suggested they direct all calls to Annika Svensson, who was in a staff meeting berating all her direct reports for failing to keep her "up-to-speed" and "in the loop."

Pulled from the meeting, she was indignant until she understood that concern was coming from the executive suites. Annika was a master of managing up and a maven of deflecting accountability for anything negative. Realizing trouble was brewing, she needed a scapegoat and decided to do some serious finger-pointing at the government relations department. Not only would they conveniently take the fall, but accusing them of being asleep at the switch might serve her well when she tried to take over the function. A crisis, she knew, was an opportunity for someone with sharp elbows.

"WTF is going on there?" Annika screamed when Snakeboots answered her call. Snakeboots had been taken aback by the audacity of a congressman writing his own legislation but couldn't admit to the client he had been blindsided. The best way to cover his ass was to allude to Washington intrigue, backroom deals, and the secret meetings he was part of, which would usually placate the client until he found out what was really going on. The old smoke and mirrors trick.

"It was a flanker movement," he apprised Annika. He then went on to describe a nonexistent clandestine meeting with Chairman Tanglewood, where they had an off-the-record discussion about Pop-Tarts in the School Breakfast program in which the two of them had agreed it would be wise to have a Republican front the issue while thumping patriotic fervor. This maneuver, he explained to Annika, took a page from the teachings of Sun Tzu, the Chinese general and war strategist.

Annika Svensson didn't have the foggiest idea what Snakeboots was talking about, but it was a storyline she could pitch to the CEO, and the Sun Tzu bit made it sound intellectual and thought out. Closing the door to the CEO's office, she cautioned him that what she was about to tell him was extremely confidential. She then parroted what Snakeboots had told her about clandestine meetings, secret deals, and Sun Tzu tactics. Not wanting to appear clueless, CEO Magpie nodded incessantly as she spoke and then sauntered over to the window to look contemplative. Finally, he looked back at her and with great solemnity instructed her to do a "deep dive" into what was going on and then "circle back" with an action plan and "ping" him when the "skill set" in their "toolbox" had been identified to address the crisis. Both left the meeting hopelessly bewildered about what either was talking about.

Kellogg issued a typical statement of corporate pablum: "We appreciate that Congressman Girtz has recognized the nutritional contribution Pop-Tarts can make as part of a complete meal. We look forward to working with him and other members of Congress to make sure the men and women of our armed forces are provided the nutritional sustenance they deserve."

CHAPTER 16

The world's most expansive and expensive sausage factory, commonly referred to as the US Congress, was getting into high gear, and pork output was expected to reach record levels. The once-banned taboo earmarks had returned with a vengeance. After all the gaseous talk about the evils of bringing home the bacon, Republicans found out that what constituents wanted you to say was not necessarily what they wanted you to do. Political necessity always triumphs over philosophy, and with a new cast of born-again earmarkers, the floodgates were open.

Snakeboots was enjoying a successful client recruitment season. The Cricket Consortium, Kellogg, and the National Hot Dog and Sausage Council all promised lucrative returns, but now he had to figure out exactly how he was going to deliver on what he had been pitching. It was time to gather some intel. This meant another lunch with the "foodies" at the Palm, and now armed with three new clients, he could expense it three times. In a way, lunch could now be considered a profit center.

Holly with the Consumer Brands Association was last to arrive, and she was spitting nails. She was vice-chair of a loose coalition of female lobbyists who called themselves Tits for Taxes, a sobriquet they justifiably deserved, as a group of professionals who specialized in advocacy with members of the tax-writing Ways and Means Committee. Just that morning, one of her group, who represented the Progressive Women's Alliance (PWA), had called on the group to formally request that the Ways and Means Committee undertake a study of so-called Pink Taxes. Now, Pink Taxes are not really taxes in the normal sense, but an upcharge for products marketed to women with only a cosmetic difference from the less expensive product directed at men. Think shampoo, razors, and body wash.

The PWA lobbyist went on to explain how the consumer product companies that make and market these products are managed by "male chauvinist pigs in positions of privilege who systematically exploit women," a charge which raised Holly's ire. She stood to remind her that the CEO of the largest company in her trade association was a woman and that any report on Pink Taxes would be filled with "demagoguery, falsehood, and misconceptions." After this retort, the PWA advocate looked Holly in the eye and charged that she was nothing but "a two-bit hooker fronting for male economic subjugation of women." The meeting ended in pandemonium after Holly cold-cocked Ms. PWA with her Louis Vuitton purse and stormed out the door, declaring the meeting adjourned until some of her fellow members had become "house trained."

Once Holly quit hyperventilating, Snakeboots ordered her a double Chardonnay. He, Charlie Harrison of the Food Marketing Institute (FMI), and Randy Lesher of the American Farm Bureau (AFB) had just about finished their first round of drinks, and if they reloaded her with a double, they would all be working at the same altitude.

The four food lobbyists kicked into the requisite pro forma discussion, lamenting the advent of a new Congress and how acrimonious and unproductive it would be, making their jobs all the more difficult. Invariably one of them would use the phrase "in this town" when describing what was going on, conveying smugness and insider knowledge. True to form, at this juncture, someone would reference the good ol' days when Ronald Reagan and Tip O'Neill would demonize each other during the day and have a beer together at night. Somehow all the vilification during the day was assuaged by a couple of cold ones after work, with both knowing full well that all the attack ads, disparaging speeches, and general insults would recommence first thing in the morning.

Intel and gossip sharing are at the heart of every lobbyist's lunch, and Snakeboots, Holly, Charlie, and Randy were no different. Snakeboots was especially keen on getting the skinny on the new upstart, Representative Mickey Girtz (R-FL), and what was behind the Pop-Tart MRE proposed legislation. He also was anxious for some thoughts on how to get Representative Barb Breen (R-GA) riled up to attack Representative Lucy Sprout (D-CA) over the Cricket Consortium and Representative Liz Pendergast (D-RI) jacked up about National Hot Dog Day. The opposition by those two would almost guarantee passage. His job as a lobbyist was to put out the bait and set the trap.

Charlie Harrison was a great source of dirt on Republican members. His girlfriend did opposition research for the Democratic Congressional Campaign Committee (DCCC), so it was her job to find out every scandalous tidbit in the past or present of every Republican candidate to serve as the basis for attack ads. The truth was not a criterion. Rumor, gossip, and innuendo all qualified for political ads in which those charged were automatically deemed guilty by the viewing public. Only in Washington would the foibles of politicians be considered scintillating pillow talk, as it was with Charlie and his girlfriend.

According to Charlie, Representative Girtz was a loose cannon hungry for higher office. Any policy or proposal emanating from him would have more curves than a Playboy Bunny. He was an inveterate political illusionist. Word had it that young Mickey Girtz had always marveled at the kayfabe in professional wrestling, where a performance was staged as genuine or authentic. He became engrossed in the ability of wrestlers to blur reality in and out of the ring. It was stagecraft he would mimic throughout his political career. In this context, the MRE Pop-Tart legislation caught the eye of the DCCC and induced Charlie's girlfriend to do a little extra investigating. Sure, it was publicized as a pro-military piece of legislation, but its side effect would create a financial windfall for Thurston Reynolds IV, scion of the Reynolds aluminum fortune and one of the congressman's largest benefactors.

Thurston and Mickey's friendship dated back to their college days at Florida State and their membership in the PLU Club. Ardent proponents of laissez-faire capitalism, they blamed the welfare state for creating a class of students who acted as if everything should be given to them. Upon graduation, as Mickey followed in his father's footsteps in politics, Thurston used his inheritance and the proceeds from an aluminum packing company his uncle gave him to become his buddy's largest donor and chairman of Businessmen for Girtz.

The aluminum packaging company caught the curiosity of Charlie's girlfriend, and she decided to delve a little deeper. Turns out the company had only one customer and one product, and here is the rub. The one customer was Kellogg, and the one product was aluminum packaging for Pop-Tarts. If the legislation proposed by Representative Girtz became law, Thurston Reynolds IV would make millions. The passage of this legislation would be the political equivalent of legal grand larceny. By connecting these dots, Snakeboots now knew who was pulling the levers behind the scenes. The public would assume Kellogg was behind the Girtz legislation, when in fact it was a nondescript little packaging company that had a congressman as a wholly owned subsidiary.

Snakeboots had learned what he needed to know about Representative Girtz, so he changed the conversation to Congresswoman Lucy Sprout and her cricket bill. Randy Lesher of the American Farm Bureau tracked every bill relating to farms and farming, and this unusual proposal about crickets warranted some attention. What impact would it have on his members? Would it be a source of new members or perceived as a competing trade association? If the latter, Snakeboots knew that AFB would pull out the stops to have it defeated. It was tough enough for Randy to keep the dues-paying members he had without having another trade association pulling on their purse strings.

Self-preservation is priority number one in the world of DC trade associations. Not only would Snakeboots need for AFB to sign off on the legislation, he would need their active support to get it passed, and the fact it would not harm AFB would not be enough to trigger their working for passage of the legislation. There had to be something positive in it for them, and the ultimate carrot was new members, so he teed up just that.

Snakeboots, with a glint in his eyes, focused on Charlie and suggested he think of the consortium as the trade association equivalent of a kayfabe in a WWE wrestling event that they had just alluded to in their discussion about Representative Girtz. Sure, Rod McDonell of cricket fame would be the Executive Director, but he was only the front man. The consortium would be run by the board that Snakeboots would handpick and control. The first order of business by the board would be a requirement that all members of the consortium must be dues-paying members of AFB. In addition to new members, Snakeboots would provide back-channel access for Randy and AFB to have input in any significant consortium board decisions. It would be a new front group at the beck and call of AFB when generating support the for policies and legislation they wanted.

This was music to Randy's ears. New members meant more dues. More dues meant a bigger budget and more compensation for him and his executive team. He always claimed he couldn't be bought, but he could be rented, and this was a rental agreement that sure fit the bill. Done deal. AFB would support the creation of a Cricket Consortium, as the press announcement would proclaim, "For the betterment of American farmers."

Watching Snakeboots and Randy create the unlikely alliance between AFB and the Cricket Consortium put a smirk on Holly's face. She loved that they had figured out a way to undo Representatives Girtz and Breen. "Now that we have figured out how to screw Girtz and Breen, how do we put it to that looney tune Lizzie Pendergast?" she exclaimed.

"So glad you asked," responded Snakeboots. "I have just the thing that will send that left-wing lunatic over the edge. Just imagine hundreds of families gathered on the Capitol lawn for National Hot Dog Day with the Wienermobile prominently parked next to the front steps. It will be a kid-friendly event that will create positive political and media vibes for all the sponsors while reifying the Fox News phantasm that the all-American family of *Leave It to Beaver* is intact and thriving. This show of Americana will also launch Ms. Pendergast and her coterie into a manic frenzy. All this at no financial cost or heavy lifting by you or your organizations. All you need to do is list yourself as a platinum sponsor, crank up your media department, and on the q.t. inform members of Congress that attendance will be considered a positive for fundraising purposes."

Charlies, Randy, and Holly exchanged glances. No cost, no heavy lifting, and a no-brainer way to demonstrate to their membership what DC insiders they were. "Count us in," they chimed in while clinking glasses in recognition of the new alliance.

"How about another round?" suggested Snakeboots.

CHAPTER 17

Molly Mustard and Peter Pork were living the dream of every college student as summer Hot Doggers, driving the Wienermobile. They were able to "haul buns" around the country to attend hundreds of "meat and greets" while being "frank" with adoring fans at fairs, carnivals, sporting events, and other mass gatherings. Armed with unlimited swag, they ingratiated themselves with every demographic while being featured in an uncountable number of selfies and subject to innumerable lame hot dog jokes. (Why do all hot dogs look alike? Because they are "in bread.")

They had traveled most of the USA, but never in their wildest dreams did they ever imagine driving the Wienermobile to Washington, DC, as the featured attraction of National Hot Dog Day. This was an opportunity of historic proportions and the pinnacle of success for a hot dogger. It did, however, come with strict protocols befitting the national stage they would be ascending. The two were flown to Oscar Mayer headquarters in Pittsburgh for three days of intensive briefings by a small army of PR consultants organized by corporate higher-ups as a CYA hedge against responsibility should this whole event go to hell in a handbasket. This was going to be the classic corporate event where success would have a thousand fathers and failure would be an orphaned child.

Per the consultants, Peter and Molly were under explicit

instructions to stay apolitical and away from anything or anybody that might be controversial. It was also emphasized that they were not to deviate from their designated route and that timing was critical for maximum media coverage.

They were to enter Washington for what was dubbed "Operation Dog Day in DC" by driving over the Fourteenth Street Bridge from Virginia, cutting across the mall by the Washington Monument, and turning left on Constitution Avenue, paralleling the mall. Once past the National WWII Memorial and Vietnam Memorial, they were to proceed left and go around the Lincoln Memorial, pass alongside the Martin Luther King Jr. Memorial and the FDR Memorial, and then continue over the small bridge over the water connecting the Tidal Basin with the Potomac River. After arriving behind the Jefferson Memorial, they would proceed to Independence Avenue, where they would turn right, passing numerous Smithsonian museums before entering the Capitol parking lot where a faux John Philip Sousa Band would be playing "The Stars and Stripes Forever." The timing of the band was of critical importance, according to the corporate controller sitting in on the briefing, since the union contract stipulated that if the performance began or lasted beyond noon, it would be deemed overtime and the band members would be entitled to triple pay.

It was a spectacular midmorning scene for Molly and Peter as they cruised across the Potomac River on the Fourteenth Street Bridge. The dome of the Capitol was prominent over the rooftops on a cloudless day. Four stops with TV/radio/print media coverage were planned. The first stop was near the Washington Monument, capturing the mall with the Capitol as a backdrop; the second was to be in front of the FDR Memorial; a third stop had a view of the iconic Jefferson Memorial in the background; and finally, the designated DEI stop on Independence Avenue in front of the National Museum of the American Indian as a centerpiece. Assembled at each location would be a gathering of what the press release referred to as "real Americans" who appreciated and recognized the contribution of hot dogs to the American experience. Organizing each group of "real Americans" was the responsibility of a subcontractor, Woke Diversification Identity Politics LLC, which specialized in providing paid actors representing a cross section of America or, as their website claimed, "diverse enough to pass muster with the woke mob and the editorial page of the *New York Times.*"

Peter and Molly were limited to only five minutes at each stop to pass out free hot dogs, distribute wiener whistles, and take selfies. By limiting each stop to five minutes, they would enter the Capitol parking lot on time and allow Fox News to do a cutaway at the FDR Memorial entitled, "Hot Dogs for Breakfast," featuring two blonde children and a Lassie look-alike dog. Keeping to the strict schedule would also allow CNN to film "How Sausage Making Represents a Diversified America" in front of the American Indian Museum.

The first stop, at the Washington Monument, was a PR home run. All the political pundits agreed it was a scene reminiscent of the famous Ronald Reagan campaign ad "Morning in America." It simply got your patriotic juices flowing!

The scene was a cross section of school children who had been recruited from the United Nations day care center waving American flags while the Oscar Mayer jingle played over the speaker system, music that reminded every adult of their childhood and how everyone loved Oscar Mayer wieners while cautioning you didn't want to be one since there would be nothing left of you!

Most of the TV reporters teared up as they recounted where they were when they'd had their first hot dog.

Molly and Peter quickly passed out free hot dogs, wiener whistles, and stickers that proclaimed hot dogs as an essential part of a balanced diet. After devouring the hot dogs, the children commenced with a cacophony of whistleblowing, singing, and screaming. Luckily only four children vomited after all this commotion, and thankfully it occurred after the Wienermobile had left, so it was off camera.

The next scheduled stop near the FDR Memorial was problematic and required a quick decision by the two hot doggers. The group gathered was to have consisted of members of the local chapter of AARP, proudly displaying wheelchairs, walkers, and canes, surrounded by an array of poster children from the Children's Defense Fund singing that Beatles favorite, "When I'm Sixty-Four," in retrospect a poor song selection since the average age was more like eighty-four and those gathered considered twenty years prior as the halcyon days of their youth.

What was to be a politically correct visual against "ageism" was marred by what loomed in the back and was the antithesis of feel-good America. On the far left were five former members of the Weather Underground wearing orange wigs and carrying placards emblazoned with *Lock Him Up* and *Mar-a-Lago Is a Rat's Nest*. Balancing this left-wing cadre on the right were six members of the Proud Boys, heavily armed, wearing red baseball caps inscribed, *Let's Go Brandon* and *Justice for the J6*. Finally, to cap off what one newscaster later capsulized as a "simple shit show" was the presence in the middle of a lanky fellow with a multicolored Afro wig carrying a placard that read, *Repent John 3:16*. Where in the world this guy came from no one could fathom, since he hadn't been seen since NFL football in the 1980s!

Panicked at this sight, Molly quickly called the command operations base and, ever careful with her language, blurted out the distress signal: "Whisky, Tango, Foxtrot!" Luckily the former marine in charge recognized the call from his military background as code for "What the fuck?" Recognizing the possibility of an optics fiasco, he directed them to forgo the FDR stop and to slow their pace to eat up the five minutes so that they would be back on schedule for the next stops and in sync with Fox News and CNN.

Per his instructions, Peter and Molly cruised past the collection of political misfits, slowed their pace, and crossed over the small bridge where the Potomac River and the Tidal Basin connect.

It was at this juncture, with time to kill, that they came upon what appeared to be an extraordinary opportunity. A small brown National Park Service sign directing tourists to the George Mason Memorial was partially covered by a makeshift marker declaring *Do Not Enter. Joey Chestnut, World Hot-Dog-Eating Champ, Commemorative Statue Under Construction.*

My God, thought Peter. Here they were with a twenty-seven-foot-long, eleven-foot-high mobile hot dog and a few minutes to spare with the opportunity to become the most famous hot doggers ever by getting a selfie with the statue of the great man himself. The first one ever! A quick right turn, two minutes for the photo, and they would be out of there. What could go wrong? It was an analysis that the marine back in the operations command center would later refer to as "the mother of all corporate FUBARS," or in other words, a fuck up beyond all recognition.

Molly reluctantly acquiesced to the diversion. Her gut told her something was just not right with the notion that Joey Chestnut would be honored on the National Mall, even as a replacement for George Mason—whoever he was. She rationalized the deviation, since the turn-off was only a few feet off the prescribed route, and it would be cool and even historic to be the first hot doggers to have a picture with the statue of America's hot dog hero. What the hell? Go for it, she figured.

Turning into the small park, they spotted a bench with an industrial-size garbage bag covering what they presumed to be a statue-like structure in the works.

They got out of the Wienermobile, approached the statue, and pulled off the garbage bag only to find to their dismay an existing statue of some revolutionary dude sitting on the bench supposedly thinking great thoughts. It clearly wasn't Joey Chestnut, so it must be the historic founding father they had never heard of—George Mason. Obviously, the project was in its infancy, and the statue of the great hot-dog-eating champion was still in development somewhere else.

Turning to return to the Wienermobile, suddenly they were confronted by two individuals in celery stalk costumes carrying duct tape and a mullet casting net, which they proceeded to throw over the two hot doggers. Tangled in the net, Peter and Molly struggled to get free but to no avail. They were bound with duct tape around their wrists and ankles, and across their mouths. Once Peter and Molly had been subdued and their phones had been confiscated, the taller of the two celery stalks informed them that they were now political prisoners of the people's army of the Animal Liberation Front.

CHAPTER 18

Forming an advocacy coalition as a front group with a patriotic name that pulls on your heartstrings to obfuscate the true purpose of the legislation is standard operating procedure in DC. If aptly named, most coalitions would be called the National Organization to Make the Participants a Lot of Money or A Group Effort to Gouge the Taxpayer. However, those organizations gathered in Snakeboots's conference room to advocate for H.R. 1776—The National Cricket Consortium Act of 2023—decided to take a more traditional approach of totally befogging its true purpose.

If you look beneath the membership veneer of each entity in a legislative advocacy group, they are somehow, some way going to make money when the bill becomes law. In this case, as in every case, the use of the term "special interest" is meaningless. Every group lobbying is a "special interest." Going around the table in Snakeboots's office, it was pretty easy to discern the vested interest of those gathered.

The National Pest Control Management Association envisioned thousands of new customers after they used social media and TV ads to incite fear of an upcoming plague of crickets attacking suburban homes as a result of lax containment measures by profiteering farmers. On the other hand, the National Fishing Association (NFA) anticipated millions of prepubescent kids taking up the sport when they consummated a tie-in with Disney. They further pictured these same kids with Jiminy Cricket cane poles, backpacks, bobbers, bait buckets, and tackle boxes, not to mention T-shirts, hats, and sunglasses licensed by NFA and emblazoned with the character.

There was obvious financial gain for the North American Coalition on Insect Agriculture with the passage of H.R. 1776. It would be a cash trove generating dues-paying members and creating a permanent foothold in the government coffers for years to come while spinning off cadres of consultants and advisors in and around Washington, DC who would become adjunct members of the coalition.

Also at the table, and poised to benefit, was the Entomological Society of America. Convention revenues would increase exponentially as all sorts of related industries would purchase booths and advertising to pitch their wares to the new customers flush with government cash. In addition, it was pretty straightforward for the American Farm Bureau. As Randy Lesher not so jokingly quipped, "Farming is farming, and we stand with the farmers so long as the farmers stand with us."

Less clearly connected but welcomed anyway to the coalition were the Association of Tomato Growers and the Gazpacho Lovers of America. Their presence would ingratiate them to a powerful member of the AG approps subcommittee who could turn on the taxpayers' financial faucet when needed. A classic—you scratch my back and I will scratch yours.

In essence, H.R. 1776—the National Cricket Consortium Act of 2023—was a transfer payment portal into the bottomless pit of the US Treasury for these organizations, all done in the name of capitalism and free enterprise.

Serving as a shill for Snakeboots during the meeting, Randy Lesher proposed that the coalition be called Americans for Food Security and Freedom to Fish. It was a classic meaningless description of what the legislation entailed, but it had the right buzzwords to strike a chord. Everyone was for food security despite not having a clue what that meant, and the freedom to fish conjured up a Norman Rockwell image of a cane pole and a small pond in rural America. It didn't matter that H.R. 1776 had nothing to do with food security or the freedom to fish. The two aspects together provided a powerful message that addressed two equally powerful constituencies—American consumers and those who fished—with little if any downside.

Once the name was adopted, Randy committed AFB to a six-figure grassroots campaign targeting the fourteen members of the AG approps subcommittee. In addition, his organization would implement a "Muzzle Maneuver" to shut the yap and opposition of Congresswoman Barb Breen (R-GA), an effort that would begin by circulating a petition at the massive new Buc-ee's truck stop and a Walmart in her district, calling on her to "Support H.R. 1776 in the House of Representatives—it is the patriotic thing to do." Following the petition drive, a print and TV ad campaign would ensue, showing Paul Revere on horseback with the enjoinder:

Paul Revere didn't let us down, and now Congresswoman Barb Breen needs to be a patriot and support H.R. 1776. Call

**her office at 202-225-WEAK and tell her
to stand tall like our forefathers. Paid
for by Americans for Food Security and
Freedom to Fish.**

While the Muzzle Maneuver was underway in
Congresswoman Barb Breen's backyard, Rod McDonell,
aka the Cricket Man, would be dispatched to the districts
of the fourteen members of the AG approps subcommittee
to drum up support for H.R. 1776. If the local member of
Congress had already committed to supporting the legislation, he or she would be honored with a trophy identifying him/her as a "Watchdog of Freedom" followed by a
fundraiser with the Cricket Man as the guest of honor. In
districts where the congressperson's support was uncertain
or wavering, the Cricket Man would hold a "Patriots Rally"
in front of the district office where a huge papier-mâché of
a flounder would be burnt in effigy with placards calling for
the congressperson to fish or cut bait.

The creation of Americans for Food Security and
Freedom to Fish had the lobbyist cabal in Snakeboots's
office stoked with a new cause that further justified their
existence. They continued to ruminate for another couple
of hours about fundraising and strategy until calling it quits
for lunch.

Upon returning to their respective offices, each organization sent out a legislative alert to the membership. These
missives routinely describe how whatever initiative is underway is being led by the sender organization and that it is
an issue of critical importance, requiring immediate action
and for recipients to contact their member of Congress with

105

this urgent message. Attached was a sample letter for them to send to their representative, which in this case called for co-sponsorship of H.R. 1776. The sample letter explained how the legislation would create thousands of jobs at no cost to the taxpayer and predicted dire consequences if it was not passed. Usually, in return, they received a response from the congressperson declaring wholehearted support or, if opposed or undecided, a commitment to keep their views in mind and disingenuously claiming how their opinion on this critical issue was important to them. In essence meaningless gibberish, but all part of the great constituent Kabuki dance that goes on in DC every day.

This was a good start for Snakeboots and the Cricket Consortium. They had a plan and the funding to implement it. Everybody was able to take credit for everything, while most everyone did nothing. Now the orchestration of public policy could begin.

CHAPTER 19

A corporate crisis reveals the mettle of a CEO. Can he or she stand tall, take the heat, and lead through adversity, or will they bend in the wind, cower in the limelight, and take the path of least resistance?

Russ Magpie, CEO of Kellogg, understood that this was a crisis that would define his legacy as Annika Svensson briefed him on the public affairs/government relations fiasco developing around Pop-Tarts. The legislation introduced by Representative Mickey Girtz (R-FL) to make Pop-Tarts part of the armed forces meals-ready-to-eat (MRE) was being lampooned and lambasted by friend and foe. Late-night comics had visuals of Tony the Tiger™ in combat fatigues, and consumer groups called the maneuver "unfettered corporate greed at the expense of military nutritional readiness." Even the product's staunchest supporters in the toaster industry attacked, declaring untoasted Pop-Tarts as simply "cardboard crud" and insisting that for the legislation to be plausible, solar-powered toasters must be included with every MRE.

Telling the truth, that they were totally blindsided by the legislation, was out of the question. Analysts would have a field day harping on managerial incompetence, and citing a flanker movement inspired by Sun Tzu would not pass the hee-haw test. The situation called for leadership. This was a moment in corporate crisis management that business schools would teach for years. The CEO of Kellogg knew that his standing in the business community would be defined by his leadership in the face of this existential threat. He would either be praised as the reincarnation of Jack Welch, who took GE to new heights, or the equivalent of Ken Lay, who steered Enron to the dustbin of ruin.

Springing into action, Russ Magpie immediately called for an emergency two-day off-site meeting to address the burgeoning crisis. Astutely recognizing it was too hot in Battle Creek in the summer for critical thinking, he ordered Human Resources to organize the conclave in Calgary, Canada, near his family's summer cabin, which would allow him to extend the stay for his annual four-week vacation.

Annika was charged with developing the program content for the Calgary off-site, which had been assigned the code name Operation Empty Calorie. It was a unique opportunity for her to consolidate her corporate power. If structured correctly, the meeting would culminate with her acquiring additional authority with more direct reports, thereby expanding people she could blame when things went south, while taking credit for successes when nothing was deserved. This was her element. She was a master of climbing the corporate ladder over the backs of others.

Dictating who and in what order they presented was key to controlling the agenda, and Annika's first call was to Dirk Dantley of the advertising firm Gray Fog Inc. He had been her ongoing supplicant since their first conversation when she explained that she could make sure he had a lot of time to spend with his family. Annika, as usual, was as cuddly as a porcupine when managing down.

She directed Dirk to develop an integrated public

relations/advertising/marketing strategy for Pop-Tarts, which would morph them from junk food status into a product exuding caring, compassion, and concern for loving parents intimately involved in their children's nutritional well-being. Whatever his plan, his obsequiousness assured that he could be counted on to add at the end of his presentation that none of it would have been possible without Annika's leadership, insight, and strategic thinking. Praise he routinely included, whether or not she had anything to do with the final work product, and critical in justifying her enhanced corporate authority.

Next to present was the Vice-President of Human Resources, who led a whiteboard discussion attempting to define organizational goals, work culture, empowerment, diversity, equity, inclusion, synergy, and whatever late-breaking HR buzzword was most current. This mind-numbing blur of corporate speak provided the opening for Annika to interject additional insipid insight that "onboarding" needed to be strategic and world-class. All these amorphous concepts were undefinable, hence unsolvable, thereby dictating the only course of action was corporate reorganization. An initiative that would necessarily involve expanding authority and direct reports for Annika.

Following the two presentations in the morning were team-building exercises meant to create corporate cohesiveness by everyone going their separate ways. Company-sponsored activities included golf, tennis, fly fishing, sight-seeing, and power shopping with Russ Magpie's wife, Tootsie. That evening, there was a dinner at Bison Bill's restaurant with a speaker from the Indigenous People's Council of Calgary, whose topic had been announced as

"Preservation of Our Natural Resources for the Future."

The second morning began with a breakfast of bacon, sausage, scrambled eggs, omelets, English muffins, and French toast, specifically chosen to demonstrate to all in attendance the challenges they faced in the breakfast category, or that was how it was explained after the hotel mistakenly served breakfast intended for the ranch hands of the Canada National Cattlemen's Convention instead of the breakfast of cereal and fruit called for in the Kellogg contract.

Speaking first on the second day after breakfast was an expert on "shrinkflation," which is a sales/marketing scam whereby you downsize the product while keeping the price the same in order to maintain your margins. The speaker came from the bubble wrap industry, which facilitated a company putting a small item or amount in a large box under the guise of preventing breakage. His presentation, "Exploiting Gullible Consumers for Fun and Profit," was a mainstay at the Bernie Madoff Institute for Business Ethics, where he was a distinguished fellow.

The next and final speaker was a representative from the Zig Ziglar Institute of Motivational Speakers, which Annika had seen advertised in an airline inflight magazine. Her presentation was an agglomeration of fundamentally meaningless inspirational and motivational exhortations, which, per the contract, she would cite as needed for the corporation to reorganize to meet its aspirations as a leader in environmental, social, and corporate governance.

Despite the fact that the offsite and reorganization did not address the Pop-Tart PR fiasco, it was a way for Russ Magpie to appear to be doing something while really doing nothing. He ordered the Human Resources department, under Annika's direction, to prepare a presentation on "Leveraging People Talent with the Use of Continuous Improvement Metrics." He further emphasized that time was of the essence, and this was to be ready when he returned in four weeks from his annual vacation at his cabin outside of Calgary. All other aspects of the Pop-Tart situation would be taken under advisement for future consideration at the next executive retreat scheduled for midwinter on Captiva Island, Florida.

Annika's corporate coup was now complete, although her title was unchanged. She had amalgamated power in the organization such that she was considered the queen bee. Her access to and influence over the CEO was not lost on all those attending the offsite. What to do about Pop-Tarts was still a conundrum, but she could hire a bevy of consultants to take care of that problem.

CHAPTER 20

It was a glorious day for the faux National Hot Dog Day underway in front of the US Capitol. Clyde Cartwright, Executive Director of the National Hot Dog and Sausage Council, and his lobbyist, P. J. "Snakeboots" Jackson, were basking in all the congressional attention they were receiving.

The word had passed through both the Republican and Democrat campaign committees that attendance was a PAC provider, meaning that stopping by the event would almost surely result in a campaign contribution from the Hot Dog Political Action Committee. In addition, each member of Congress who participated would be designated an honorary hot dog ambassador and allowed to be pictured with the Wienermobile. A picture which in turn would be distributed to the small weekly newspapers and daily shoppers, ad rags, and other such local media outlets, which would always run the photos with a puff piece accompanying it. The lure of a surefire campaign contribution and free media produced a line of more than twenty newbie members of Congress ready to pay homage to Clyde, Snakeboots, and the all-American hot dog.

While the receiving-line glad-handing was underway, Clyde's cell phone vibrated with an incoming text message. He had explicitly instructed the staff not to bother him, so he ignored the alert. After a few minutes, it began to vibrate again so, greatly irritated, he decided to check it out, thinking to himself, *Some staffer is going to pay hell for this.* He opened the text, and after one look began to sway back and forth before collapsing to the ground.

The text showed Molly Mustard and Peter Pork gagged with duct tape and strapped to a statue of some Revolutionary War–era figure sitting on a bench. Propped in front of the statue was the National Hot Dog and Sausage Council press release dated that day, outlining the Wienermobile schedule and the timeline for its travels in Washington. Standing behind Molly and Peter were what appeared to be two individuals costumed as celery stalks holding a sign declaring the two hot doggers were being held as enemies of the people for their crimes against animals and that ransom demands would follow in the next text.

Standing next to Clyde when he collapsed was his intern, Bitsy Baskin, who had earned her position by being the daughter of the Vice-President of Equity and Diversity of Ball Park Franks. Bitsy, seeing Clyde in distress, snatched the cell phone from his hand and, upon seeing the picture, let out a shriek roughly equivalent to a thermonuclear explosion. It was such a blast that the Capitol Hill police, concerned that another J6 event was underway, immediately issued a code red terrorist alert and dispatched two armored riot control (ARC) vehicles to the front lawn of the Capitol. The presence of these vehicles triggered the activation of the bomb-sniffing dog division, accompanied by mounted park rangers, who were followed by a platoon of helmeted Capitol police outfitted with riot shields and bullhorns.

Pandemonium ensued, but while this chaos was unfolding, the newbie members of Congress rushed to Snakeboots so that he could affirm their attendance at the event. Lost and forgotten in all this madness was the collapsed Clyde Cartwright and his intern Bitsy Baskin.

The bedlam in front of the Capitol captured the attention of every media outlet. Fox News questioned whether this was another 9/11 somehow connected to the Steele dossier. CNN and MSNBC held forth that all this turmoil was a result of cuts in the school feeding programs and called on the White House to organize a national conference on nutrition, free food, and national security. Newsmax questioned whether all of this could have been prevented if the public had access to Hunter Biden's laptop. Meanwhile, Gettr and Truth Social encouraged everyone to come to DC for a "wild event" with special room rates at the Trump Hotel. Finally, not to be outdone, the local CBS TV affiliate WUSA dispatched its Eye in the Sky traffic helicopter to provide live coverage of the events unfolding at the Capitol. The arrival of the helicopter further exacerbated the situation, prompting the Pentagon to scramble a squadron of F-16s from Andrews Air Force Base and the FAA to order a shutdown of all commercial and private flights within a 250-mile radius of Washington, DC.

The always attentive Bitsy carefully propped Clyde up next to a huge tree on the Capitol lawn, which was now behind the police line. She and a thoroughly confused and disoriented Clyde were the only ones who knew what had instigated the turmoil at the Capitol. Not since Wienerman, the life-size statue of a hot dog licking its lips while squeezing bottles of ketchup and mustard, had been abducted outside the Dairy Winkle restaurant in Charleston, West Virginia, had anything this dastardly occurred. The kidnapping of Wienerman had set the country on edge. The reaction to the Wienermobile being held hostage was unimaginable. The Department of Education would have to immediately dispatch grief counselors to grammar schools to help students cope with issues of anxiety, abandonment, and family estrangement. In addition, PBS most likely would respond by initiating a new episode of *Sesame Street* entitled, "When a Wiener Goes Missing." All in all, the national ramifications of this would be widespread and significant.

Slowly, the groggy Clyde started to regain consciousness, assisted by huge gulps of water from Bitsy's ever-present Yeti water bottle. Still somewhat confused and dazed, he asked what the hell had happened. She then helped him recall how he had been greeting the lined-up newbies when he received a text that the Wienermobile and the two hot doggers were being held for ransom.

Just then Clyde's text alert began to again vibrate. Fumbling with his phone, he opened the new message and was confronted with a terrifying sight. Peter Pork and Molly Mustard were still gagged with duct tape and strapped to the statue in the same location, but this time the figures costumed as celery stalks were holding a five-foot-high cardboard ransom note with demands:

Carnivore Criminals

You must adopt and implement the following animal bill of rights:

Personhood for all non-humans

Freedom from exploitation, cruelty, and neglect

Preventive health care, including mental health

Elimination of factory farming

Freedom from fear and anxiety

Full eligibility for IRA and pension benefits

Right to collectively bargain for better working conditions

Failure to comply within twenty-four hours will result in your two criminal conspirators being required to eat a hot dog every five minutes until they exceed the Joey Chestnut record of seventy-six hot dogs. This exercise will be repeated daily until our demands are met.

—Animal Liberation Front

Clyde crumbled and relapsed into a state of total unconsciousness. Bitsy once again snatched his phone from his clenched fist and upon seeing the photo let out a scream comparable to that of a dying hyena. She, too, then collapsed onto the comatose Clyde.

Meanwhile, Snakeboots had regrouped with a bevy of congressional newbies at the Capitol Hill restaurant/watering hole the Monocle. Determined not to be distracted by exigent circumstances, they were deep into a discussion on how to request campaign contributions from the Hot Dog PAC when out of the blue a disheveled and disoriented Clyde and Bitsy approached the table.

Interrupting the conversation, Clyde blurted out that

he had critical information about what had precipitated the melee on the Capitol grounds, which must be kept absolutely confidential. He stated this admonition not knowing that the kidnappers had already issued a press release and were negotiating with Chris Wallace of CNN for an exclusive interview. As is always the case when politicians heard it was to be held confidential, their first reaction was to contemplate which of their favorite news outlets they would leak it to first.

Clyde went on to explain to the group how his near-death experience had been brought on by two disturbing texts sent by unidentifiable sources. The first was a picture of the two hot doggers gagged with duct tape and strapped to the mystery statue with two figures costumed as celery stalks standing behind them. The next text was the same assemblage, but this time with a ransom note with a list of demands signed by the Animal Liberation Front.

It was stunned silence as Clyde passed the texts around the table for viewing. Snakeboots finally spoke up, advising the group that this was an act of war, and in war, you never know when or where your next meal might come from so, he said, "Let's order."

After ordering, each newbie would momentarily excuse themselves to "check in with the office" or take a call from a "big contributor," so they could leak this info before they got scooped. Within minutes, news alerts citing "unnamed sources" were bleating on cell phones and iPads about a kidnapping that was being compared to that of Lindbergh's baby being abducted in 1932. A sonorous Tucker Carlson warned that the American way of life was under attack.

The *Wall Street Journal* issued a stock alert, resulting in a collapse of meat futures and a run on Impossible Foods, Beyond Meat, and other meat alternatives. Jim Cramer of *Mad Money* screamed that stock in Ted Turner's Montana Grill restaurants would be as worthless as Confederate money. The White House, trying to stay ahead of the curve, issued a statement "deriding this act of terrorism as an attack on every hot-dog-eating American" while calling on every red-blooded American, vegetarian or not, to unite in solidarity against this common enemy. Laura Ingraham weighed in with a warning that the Animal Liberation Front was a mouthpiece for the deep state and that a national ban on hot dogs was imminent. Panic buying of hot dogs ensued, which resulted in the near elimination of the product from grocery shelves.

The nation was gripped in fear, and in response, the FBI announced the creation of a task force to doggedly track down the perpetrators. Requests for help went out to the general public, asking them to call the FBI or their local police if anything resembling a twenty-seven-foot hot dog on wheels was spotted. In addition, they asked for help in determining who and where the statue in the ransom picture was located. Finally, they updated the FBI's ten most wanted list in every post office in the country to include a picture of two figures costumed as celery stalks.

Following a lunch of soft-shelled crabs and creamed spinach, a semi-coherent Clyde, Bitsy, and Snakeboots huddled in the Hot Dog Council offices to assess the damages. All of a sudden the phone began ringing off the hook from member companies saying sales were off the charts and never had they seen such attention paid to hot dogs. Clyde and Bitsy were unsure what to do, but Snakeboots knew.

He realized they had stumbled upon the marketing coup of the century. Just feign the whole thing was planned and declare victory.

CHAPTER 21

Snakeboots liked to operate in the shadows, and nothing created a bigger shadow than the Brobdingnagian mother of all spending legislation, the omnibus appropriations bill. It was the legislative lode of lard, filled with every piece of pork that members of the House and Senate Appropriations Committees could imaginably foist on the unsuspecting public. It also procedurally created an opportunity to pass legislation with the consent of only the House or Senate, once again proving the old adage "There is no honor among thieves." A scenario made possible by the unwritten rule that the Senate would not object to what the House slipped in and vice versa. Sure, certain members of Congress would rant and rave on cable TV about specifics, the process, and so on, but at the end of the day, the whole big package would pass, oftentimes with those protesting the loudest, getting the most. There was no shame, and stealth was the name of the game.

The omnibus appropriations bill had been the target for Snakeboots and the National Cricket Consortium since the get-go. The math was quite simple. The House Subcommittee on Agricultural Appropriations had fourteen members—nine Republicans and five Democrats. All you needed were eight members to support or acquiesce to funding the consortium. The process was also quite simple. Park the funding provision in the massive bill at its inception, when it was marked up in the subcommittee. Stay quiet as the money train leaves the station and chugs down the legislative tracks without drawing attention to what it did or what it cost. Not becoming a cynosure was critical, and this is where grassroots lobbying comes into play. Visit a congressional district to get the representative to either support the funding provision or make it so that objecting to it was not politically worth their while. Silence was tantamount to support.

The Cricket Man grassroots political roadshow would start in Bismarck, North Dakota, the home of the subcommittee chairman, Mark Tanglewood, and would be accompanied by a plethora of "Paul Revere" ads on local TV stations. Sure, Chairman Tanglewood had already assured Snakeboots of his support, but it was important to create the appearance of objectivity to an issue that was prewired. The notion of "sound science" was always a safe refuge, and the place to start was the University of North Dakota (UND). Practically every professor in the Ag Department of UND was on the dole with federal research grants, and it was just a question of which one was rentable and available for this project.

One professor stood out. Eminently qualified as an entomological expert, Dr. Klaus Schmidt was known for breakthrough research into how mosquitos are a disruptive factor at picnics in North Dakota. Contacted by Chairman Tanglewood's staff, and after a five-minute briefing on the phone, he issued a scientific summary of the proposed National Cricket Consortium legislation, concluding that "the bill was of critical importance to the economic well-being of every North Dakotan," and it would "serve as a lure to attract migrant farm workers interested in fishing." The reference to migrant workers was a sop to Congressman Tanglewood, who was trying to do a political pivot after years of advocating a wall on the Mexican border and after being informed by the North Dakota Sugar Beet Association that the entire crop would rot in the fields without illegal workers.

The summary was embargoed for release to coincide with Cricket Man's appearance at the local Cabela's. Accompanied by a local Brad Paisley imitator singing the star's famous fishing song, "I'm Gonna Miss Her." The good professor's paper could have claimed the world was flat, and no one would have paid heed.

Suffice it to say, the arrival of Cricket Man and the eventual release of the scientific summary was impactful. The *Bismarck Tribune* took note of the scientific underpinnings of the consortium legislation, and the fact that such a renowned figure as Cricket Man had come to North Dakota was a testimonial to the clout and prestige of their very own Congressman Mark Tanglewood. The newspaper would go on to mention that they could think of no one more deserving than Mark Tanglewood to receive the coveted designation Watchdog of Freedom being awarded to him by the prestigious Americans for Food Security and Freedom to Fish.

That evening, a fundraiser was held for Chairman Mark Tanglewood with Cricket Man as the guest of honor. Participants included the President of the University of North Dakota, Dr. Klaus Schmidt, two planeloads of lobbyists from Washington, DC, a representative of the Association of Tomato Growers, the President of the Gazpacho Lovers of America, and three North Dakota farmers. It was at the conclusion of this event that Chairman Tanglewood announced with great solemnity that after lengthy and serious consideration, he had decided to support the National Cricket Consortium Act of 2023.

The next stop on the roadshow for Cricket Man was Fresno, California, the congressional district of Representative Lucy Sprout (D-CA). As a principal sponsor and token Democrat, it was critical that she be bolstered with the love of her constituents, and a little campaign cash wouldn't hurt either. The University of California-Davis was called upon to issue another scientific summary, and they in turn called upon Professor Wan Lee, known for his renowned treatise "Are Ants Attracted to Sugar?" Professor Lee, in his summary, cited "the importance of the consortium legislation to expanding welfare benefits in California" and how it had the potential to "deter fish-loving migrant workers from crossing the border, negating the need for a wall."

The *Fresno Bee* newspaper, citing the study, editorialized that passage of the legislation would free up funds to be spent on the wall for migrant education, expanded health care, and ant eradication programs. It went on to say that the presence of Cricket Man in Fresno was incontrovertible proof of the prestige and clout of their very own congresswoman, Lucy Sprout.

That evening, a fundraiser was held for Congresswoman Sprout with Cricket Man as the guest of honor. In attendance was the President of the University of California-Davis, Professor Lee, two planeloads of lobbyists from Washington, DC, a representative of the Association of Tomato Growers, the President of the Gazpacho Lovers of America, and three members of congresswoman's book club.

Concluding the fundraiser with great gravitas, Congresswoman Sprout announced, "After examining my conscience and concluding that Mexico will not pay for the wall—and if they did, it would be of poor quality—it struck me that I needed to act and act decisively. Therefore, I will introduce and work toward passage of the National Cricket Consortium Act of 2023."

It was then that she was awarded designation as a Watchdog of Freedom by the esteemed Americans for Food Security and Freedom to Fish, a presentation that was met with rapturous applause.

Back in DC, Snakeboots was holding court under his caricature on the wall at the Palm restaurant with a potential new client. Representatives of the Evel Knievel School of Motor Safety had come to see him in search of Department of Transportation funding for a high school safe driving course they had developed. It was always a good day when he had a potential new client in town, and already two members of Congress had stopped by and offered to help in any way they could. However, what started off as a good day quickly came to an end when he received a text from his admin, Ruby, that he needed to return immediately to his office for "damage control" concerning a breaking bad news story on Cricket Man.

Breaking bad news was an understatement. *Bass Master*, the nationally syndicated fishing TV show, was about to release an investigative report done in collaboration with *60 Minutes* exposing a multiyear scheme by Cricket Man to fraudulently win hundreds of bass tournaments. According to the *Bass Master/60 Minutes* exposé, Cricket Man would routinely fill the bellies of fish he allegedly caught with split shot, lug nuts, and assorted household trash to inflate their weight before being put on the scale. A video of him "fish packing," as he called it, was leaked by his jilted former girlfriend, who was a checkout person at Captain D's Seafood Kitchen and who cited her background in the seafood industry as making her an incontrovertible expert on anything related to fish or fishing.

The video was damning evidence. Cricket Man could be seen shoving the split shot, lug nuts, and a variety of other items down the mouth of all different sizes of bass, transforming them into something resembling baby manatees. In the audio accompanying the video, you could hear his former girlfriend comment that the bass was starting to look like some sort of mutant undersea monster, to which Cricket Man responded, "All the other fisherman and judges are dumb fucks who won't know the difference."

Social media exploded with outrage over Cricket Man and what was now being called Fishgate. CNN quickly assembled a panel with John Dean, Bob Woodward, and Carl Bernstein to discuss whether Fishgate might erode confidence in our institutions the way Watergate had. Fox News questioned whether any of this would have happened if the content of Hunter Biden's laptop had been available. Facebook and Twitter banned as fake news any fish stories regarding the size and length of fish caught. Finally, the White House, so as not to appear flat-footed, issued a statement that the weight of any fish caught while participating in a federally sanctioned fishing contest, under minimums set by the Department of the Interior, would be deemed suspect if the belly contained split shot, lug nuts, or household trash.

Snakeboots called an emergency meeting of the Americans for Food Security and Freedom to Fish to discuss the ever-widening scandal. The newly released videotape recorded by Cricket Man's hell-bent-to-get-even former girlfriend also had him commenting that "fishermen are inherently stupid, and those folks who run the tournaments are even dumber." In the tape, he goes on to say, "Thank God there is no cure for stupid." It didn't matter that the former girlfriend was trailer trash, her Captain D's credentials were impeccable, and her protestations that Cricket Man was a low-life scumbag resonated with every woman who had ever been dumped by a boyfriend, resulting in her Facebook page receiving thousands of Likes. Someone had even linked her site to an article called, "How To Kill Your Boyfriend and Keep Partying." It didn't matter what awards he had won when he was on tape calling everybody in the industry "dumbfucks," "stupid," and essentially witless. This was ugly, and all agreed it could get uglier without some serious damage control and spin.

There was palpable angst among those gathered in Snakeboots's conference room. Randy Lesher addressed the group by suggesting that they needed a new spokesperson to ensure that coverage of Fishgate was short-lived. His comments and use of the words *spokesperson*, *ensure*, and *coverage* prompted a vigorous and animated discussion about retaining an easily recognizable TV insurance personality.

The first suggestion was Flo from the Progressive Insurance ads, who would arguably assuage women but might be threatening to male egos. Next was Jake from State

Farm Insurance, who would convey a sense of inclusion and diversity but who might be considered too woke and raise concerns among Southerners who still believed in the lost cause of the Confederacy. Then they discussed the old guy with Farmers Insurance, who would be calming but was dismissed as having the charisma of a speed bump, and then the fellow with the deep voice for Allstate Insurance reminding everyone they were in good hands was rejected as too easily being confused as a voice from heaven or a spokesperson for the Christian Coalition. Limu Emu with Liberty Mutual Insurance was considered too wacky, and the Geico Gecko might get mistaken for bait. Finally, the Mayhem Man for Allstate was dismissed as perpetuating a state of chaos that already existed. Nobody knew what to do.

As the meeting was about to unravel into a verbal free-for-all, Snakeboots took the floor to emphatically declare it was time to implement the Jedi mind trick, or what had been known in the past as the 4Rs—reject, religion, redemption, and revival. Sure, there would be costs involved in retaining rentable ministers and faith-based institutions, but such costs would be de minimis compared to the collapse of the Cricket Consortium undertaking. Everyone nodded in agreement, although no one really knew what he was talking about. Finally, one participant had the temerity to ask, "What the hell is the Jedi mind trick?"

Snakeboots then explained that the Jedi mind trick was a foolproof way to totally disorient the public through a series of bold-faced lies, half-truths, verbal misdirections, and heavenly appeals. In this case, Cricket Man would categorically reject the accusations against him as "totally untrue," but then invoke religion by roughly quoting the

Bible, "Let him who is without sin throw the first stone." This would then be followed by a declaration that he had seen the light on the road to redemption and that all should join him as he atoned for his sins. Finally, at some point, he would blame the whole mess on fake news generated by the lame/liberal media.

The cognitive dissonance created by denying something, then claiming absolution from what you didn't do, and then attributing the whole mess to some outside force would guarantee total befuddlement by the American public. Considering the average American had the attention span of a gnat, they would soon forget the whole episode and go back to obsessing over important things like what the Kardashians were wearing.

There was stunned silence in the conference room until the President of the Entomological Society shouted out, "Brilliant" followed by others exclaiming, "Masterful," and one participant crediting Snakeboots with being the "doctor of duplicity." The support for implementing the Jedi mind trick was unanimous. Now all they had to do was issue a statement by Cricket Man encompassing the 4Rs along with a reference to fake news and the lame/liberal media and then go rent a couple of ministers and a faith-based institution or two.

CHAPTER 22

Her title as Senior Vice-President of Nutrition Marketing, Family Values, and Customer Welfare did not really reflect the true power Annika wielded after the corporate reorganization. She had finally attained the coveted corporate plateau where those who do the least get the most. Reporting to her would be teams of subservient staff and obsequious outside consultants at her beck and call. Fear would be the motivating factor. She was the unabashed master of "quiet firing," a technique where she would ostracize and humiliate someone until they left and then profess concern, surprise, and remorse over their departure.

She had successfully bamboozled her CEO, Russ Magpie, with the Sun Tzu bit when Representative Mickey Girtz caught her by surprise with the Pop-Tarts MRE legislation. She had feigned knowledge of the legislative process but now needed Snakeboots more than ever to guide her through the DC morass. Pivoting from the School Breakfast program to another financial funnel was not a problem just so long as at the end of the day the government, in the name of free enterprise, helped them sell more Pop-Tarts.

Snakeboots was at his spin doctor best when Annika called looking for guidance and some swamp language she could use to explain away the MRE legislation and how it fit into a master plan even though no such plan existed. He reiterated his belief in the philosophy of Sun Tzu and how their next move must involve gaslighting the issue of Pop-Tarts in any government program while creating a state of political cognitive dissonance. In other words, create total confusion so that the question became where Pop-Tarts fit in, not if. This would allow politicians to do what they do best, i.e. fix a problem that did not exist.

In order to create a state of congressional dubiety, the first step was to get Representative Barb Breen to introduce legislation mandating Pop-Tarts as part of the School Breakfast program. A known disrupter, she would jump at the chance to shove it down the throats of the liberals and bask in all the accolades she would receive from Truth Social, Parler, Gettr, and the rest of right-wing social media, and with a little bit of luck she might get mentioned during *The Five* on Fox News. This in turn would incentivize the chaos caucus, which she chaired, to demand a Pop-Tart provision in any must-do legislation, like raising the debt ceiling or funding the military in Ukraine.

Once Representative Breen had introduced her bill, all hell would break loose with the likes of Representative Lizzie Pendergast and the flame-throwing fantasists of the left who would proclaim we had reached nutritional Armageddon. They would instinctively schedule a press conference with the Center for Science in Our Own Interest to demand that the Department of Justice, the Federal Trade Commission, the Food and Drug Administration, and the Department of Agriculture launch an inquiry into the "sales, marketing, and distribution" of Pop-Tarts. During the press conference, they would go on to claim that implementation of the School Breakfast legislation would sow misunderstanding and mistrust among political thought leaders, thereby thwarting the creation of a "Natural Nanny for Nutrition," which, according to them, the nation desperately needed.

The liberals and Progressive clerisy, by overplaying their hands, would provide the fodder for Fox News, Newsmax, and One America to pounce. They would equate the attack on Pop-Tarts as a direct assault on American families, moms, motherhood, and a suburban life devoid of crime, hunger, and destitution. Soon Pop-Tarts would start tracking on social media with Critical Race Theory (CRT), school library books, and Hunter Biden's laptop. Pop-Tarts would become a national issue and the elixir for every ill facing American society.

Annika listened intently and took notes as Snakeboots laid out this political scenario. She was especially impressed and excited when he quoted Sun Tzu as advising, "In the midst of chaos, there is also opportunity." This would allow her to impress CEO Magpie and create the impression she actually knew what she was doing. It would make her sound profound when she actually didn't have a clue how any of this was going to help sell Pop-Tarts.

Pretending to understand, she innocently asked Snakeboots, "What comes next?"

Ever prepared, Snakeboots was ready with another Sun Tzu quote: "Build your opponent a golden bridge to retreat across."

"And how do we do that?" responded Annika.

"Easy," responded Snakeboots. "Speaker McCrudy."

According to Snakeboots, the Speaker detested Representatives Girtz, Breen, and Pendergast and would do whatever it took to make sure none of them was successful. His problem was that if both Girtz and Breen failed to have Pop-Tarts included in MREs or the School Breakfast program, then Pendergast would succeed and declare victory. "So," Snakeboots said, "we have to build them the bridge that Sun Tzu referred to so that once all of them have retreated across it, they can spin it any way they want."

"And exactly how do we build this bridge?" asked Annika quizzically.

"Simple," responded Snakeboots. "We put Pop-Tarts on the space shuttle."

Now Annika was totally confounded and question-ing whether she was listening to the musings of a madman. That was, until Snakeboots set the stage on how all this would play out.

He went on to explain that Speaker McCrudy ruled with an iron fist and was always amenable to a good suggestion as to how to flatten those who don't toe the line. "If we tee up the idea of putting Pop-Tarts on the space shuttle as a way to kneecap Girtz, Breen, and Pendergast simultaneously," Snakeboots argued, "he will be on it in a nanosecond. All he will need to do is call the head of NASA with the suggestion. The head of NASA is a former member of Congress who knows the Speaker's clout and is attuned to the fact that he needs his support to get funding for NASA."

Pop-Tarts would not be part of Meals-Ready-To-Eat, and they would not be included in the School Breakfast program, but on the other hand, Congresswoman Pendergast would fail to keep them out of a federal program. A trifecta for the Speaker.

What he was unfolding was starting to click with Annika. She remembered years ago Coke and Pepsi had fought tooth and nail for the bragging rights of having been the first soft drink in space. If she could pull off having Pop-Tarts in space, she would be considered a marketing genius. The juxtaposition of Pop-Tarts vs. Tang, the God-awful orange juice substitute that astronauts had to drink, would make Pop-Tarts look like a health food. The publicity surrounding this would be a boon to the whole toaster pastry category, with Kellogg getting the lion's share. They could run ads touting Pop-Tarts as extraterrestrial food to be consumed on earth or in the heavens by the next generation of astronauts. Maybe even do a tie-in with Girl Scouts and Boy Scouts working on a space badge and as part of their fundraising activities; they could sell them like they did cookies and nuts. The hype would be priceless.

She had one last question for Snakeboots: "What about Girtz, Breen, and Pendergast?"

Always ready with an answer, he responded, "No problem. Politicians never admit defeat. After they cross that golden bridge we built them, they will position it so they somehow won. Everyone declares victory." Confident of success, as he always was, he had one last note of caution. "Always expect the worst, and rarely will you be disappointed. Now, with that one caveat, what do you think?"

Annika had a one-word reply to Snakeboots. "Launch."

CHAPTER 23

Snakeboots had left the offices of the Hot Dog Council mumbling something about omnibus approps, Pop-Tarts, and crickets, leaving Clyde and Bitsy to their own devices. Clyde still seemed confused and disoriented, making Bitsy realize there was a power vacuum and with a little finagling she could assume command. Bitsy prided herself as a student of US politics and remembered reading in her course on American history that when President Ronald Reagan was shot, former general Alexander Haig announced in the White House not to worry: "I am in control here." Sure, his declaration incited fear that a military coup had taken place, but to Bitsy, it was a cool maneuver that just happened to ruffle a few feathers. It brought to mind the inscription above the National Archives Building: *Past Is Prologue*. To her, this was her Haig moment, when she could assume control.

Before departing, Snakeboots had advised them to simply declare victory. Hot dog sales were rocketing, and the member companies were ecstatic. Now Bitsy needed to figure out how to keep the hype up, free the captive hot doggers, and parlay all this into something in DC memorializing hot dogs, all the while cementing her position as leader of the council.

Nowhere in the line of succession at the National Hot Dog and Sausage Council is there any provision for an intern to wrest command from the Executive Director.

This lack of specific authority did not prevent Bitsy from filling the void. She issued an official declaration on council stationery to the board of directors that the Executive Director was "cognitively incapacitated" and that exigent circumstances dictated she assume the position of Executive Director in Extremis of the National Hot Dog and Sausage Council. Upon receipt, after confirming the annual golf outing was still intact, the board, consistent with most trade association boards, capitulated to those in DC with "insider knowledge" and allowed a twenty-two-year-old intern to take charge of the organization.

Bitsy knew her first task was to secure the release of Molly Mustard and Peter Pork. Recalling her World History seminar and how damaging the Iranian hostage situation was to the presidency and the non-reelection of Jimmy Carter, she was determined that her term as Executive Director would not suffer a similar fate. Bitsy also recalled from her undergrad seminar Marketing and Successful Consumer Deception 101 that the association of a product with death, maiming, and other unpleasantness was not a positive attribute and could be a deterrent to sales.

Determined to make fact-based decisions, she called the dean of the Department of Food Science at Cornell University to inquire as to the impact on the human body of eating seventy-six hot dogs for consecutive days. The prognosis was grim. According to the dean, after just one day, someone would show symptoms of gastritis, which include abdominal bloating, pain, and indigestion. The second day, they would have intensified symptoms, but also vomiting and delirium. If still surviving, after a third day, they would in all likelihood enter a comatose state brought about by what is commonly referred to as hot dog revulsion syndrome.

Upon hearing the report from Cornell, Bitsy astutely determined that widespread media reports of hot dog revulsion syndrome would not be good for sales. This meant she had two days to secure Molly and Peter's release. She would need to act and act fast, or her tenure as Executive Director would be Carter-ized.

Thinking the kidnapping might have been an inside job, Bitsy placed a call to the United Fresh Fruit and Vegetable Association to see if they might be missing a couple of celery costumes. Used to having her calls ignored as an intern, she was pleasantly surprised when they returned the call, asking to speak to the Executive Director in Extremis. The response, however, was disappointing. Turns out the two celery costumes had been donated years ago to the theater department at Iowa State University in Ames for the musical *There Is no Substitute for Meat*. The costumes were reported stolen after the show was canceled, following a sit-in by vegan student activists.

The report of the costumes' whereabouts was not only disappointing but rather odd. Iowa State was where Clyde had gone to college. Obviously, just a coincidence, but a strange one.

While Bitsy was taking stock of the situation, the FBI put out an all points bulletin (APB) for everyone to be on the lookout for a twenty-seven-foot hot-dog-like vehicle and anyone dressed as a celery stalk. The FBI also had their crime lab contact the University of Virginia Revolutionary War studies program to see if they might be able to identify the puzzling statue to which Peter and Molly had been attached. In addition, the FBI Media and Promotions division requested help from the TV show *America's Most Wanted*, who immediately began running teasers for an upcoming new show, *Finding Dead Doggers*, sponsored by the Psychic Readers Academy, whose website claimed it would enable someone to find anybody anywhere.

The media circus had begun, and Bitsy was omnipresent as the insightful insider intern. Everywhere she appeared, she warned of a coming national shortage of hot dogs and the threat of a ban resulting in a wienerless country. She even tweeted that someday adults might find themselves at cocktail parties without pigs in a blanket as appetizers. The doomsday scenario she painted was accentuated by Tucker Carlson, who suggested that forces on the left planned to substitute tofu bars for hot dogs at Major League Baseball games, further destroying the America we love and know. The hysteria surrounding hot dogs created a run on the product, stripping grocery store refrigerators of "tube steaks" and forcing major chains to put a two-package limit on customer purchases. Long lines formed outside of Publix, Kroger, Safeway, and other major food chains, further escalating the hysteria. All this mania forced the White House to declare a national health emergency and invoke the Defense Production Act "to insure an ample supply of tubular pork so the cholesterol level of the nation does not get dangerously low."

The FBI hotline was abuzz with tips from around the country, but to no avail. Sightings of celery people were reported as far away as Alaska, and one tip that seemed to have promise regarding the Wienermobile turned out to be the Big Idaho Potato Truck after a state police SWAT team was dispatched to a Nebraska truck stop to investigate.

Finally, however, there was a breakthrough. A hot dog vendor on the National Mall was approached by two people dressed as celery stalks who ordered 152 hot dogs with ketchup and mustard. As a longtime vendor, he thought nothing of it until they came back the next day and ordered seventy-six with ketchup and seventy-six with mustard only. This change caught his attention. It was very unusual for repeat customers to change condiments. Something was amiss.

That evening while watching *Jeopardy* with his wife, he mentioned the two celery people and how strange it was for them to change condiments. Turns out his wife was an aficionado of a Crime Stoppers Facebook page where the Oscar Mayer Company had posted a ten-thousand-dollar award for leads resulting in the arrest of people dressed like celery stalks and the safe return of the two hot doggers. The Facebook posting went on to promise another five thousand dollars and a year's supply of Oscar Mayer all-beef hot dogs for a lead resulting in the return of the Wienermobile. His wife, going on the keen observations of her husband, immediately called the Oscar Mayer customer service number, which was answered by a call center in Mumbai. The operator had a hard time with English and wrote up her message as "someone stalking celery at the National Mall" while seeking "beef dogs," to which the operator responded, "Cows are sacred in India, so no beef dogs."

Meanwhile, at the University of Virginia, the FBI crime lab team was utilizing state-of-the-art facial recognition technology on research documents in the Revolutionary War department to see if they could find a match for the statue. If they could find a match, it would tell them who it was a statue of and then lead them to where it was. It was tedious gumshoe work, but necessary.

Fatefully, one of the student geeks recruited to run the facial computer program had recently visited DC with the Chess Club. While touring the National Mall, he was on the lookout for a secluded spot where he could peel off from the group and smoke some weed. As they were approaching the Jefferson Memorial, he spotted a deserted cul-de-sac with a National Park Service sign indicating it was the George Mason Memorial. He had no idea who Mason was, but this spot was the perfect place to smoke some grass, since the forlorn location looked like no one had visited it in years.

Sure enough, the Mason Memorial was a pitiful monument. Nothing but a bench with some sort of George Washington look-alike statue sitting on it. He plopped down on the bench, lit a joint, and for fun took a selfie of himself with the statue to send to his girlfriend back in Charlottesville.

Something about the face of the statue he was trying to match looked vaguely familiar. So as a lark, he ran a reverse photo search. Instantly, three green lights appeared on the screen, indicating a perfect match. The statue in the Mason Memorial was the same one in the picture with the captive hot doggers. The FBI headquarters in Washington was notified immediately that they had a match.

The alert from the University of Virginia was received almost simultaneously with a tip from the Oscar Mayer consumer call center that something to do with celery stalks and beef dogs had been reported on the mall. The FBI now had almost incontrovertible circumstantial evidence that the hot doggers were being held at a memorial no one had ever heard of in Washington, DC. Not only had no one ever seen or heard of the Mason Memorial, no one had a clue where it was much less who he was.

The FBI contacted the Director of the National Park Service (NPS) to ascertain the location of the Mason Memorial. The Director of NPS admitted he had no idea but would touch base with the grounds crew to see if they had ever come across it. The manager of the mall's mowing service responded, "Yes, such a place exists, and it's nick-named Sleepy Hollow since it's where crew workers went to sleep off hangovers." Tucked away in the vicinity of the Jefferson Memorial, nobody ever went there and, according to the manager, you could hide about anything and nobody would know the difference. Perfect spot to park a rather unusual vehicle and never be seen.

The FBI Director excitedly placed a call to Clyde Cartwright, Executive Director of the National Hot Dog and Sausage Council, to alert him that they had found the hideout of the kidnappers. He was told, however, that Mr. Cartwright was "presently indisposed" and that he would be directed to Bitsy Baskin, Executive Director in Extremis.

Bitsy was encouraged by the news but concerned about what would come next when the Director informed her that a joint FBI/DC police SWAT team was being organized to storm the location. Numerous fatalities and injuries were not optics that would be conducive to hot dog sales. Nor would two hot doggers suffering from hot dog revulsion syndrome be a positive image for the product line. She needed to secure their release before the syndrome kicked in after eating seventy-six hot dogs on consecutive days and before the SWAT team went into action. She needed time to think. She thought to herself, *What would former secretary of state Madeleine Albright do in this situation?*

Then she recalled from her sophomore year US military affairs class entitled "Vietnam: A War We Really Won," about how Henry Kissinger had established a back channel to negotiate with the North Vietnamese. Maybe if she could take a page out of his playbook and establish a back channel with the kidnappers, they could resolve this standoff before a third day of hot dog consumption with all its dire consequences. Bitsy began to fantasize that if she could pull this off. she would be considered the Henry Kissinger of the trade association world and possibly be awarded the Nobel Peace Prize like he was. However, time was of the essence, and she needed to get going to get this done. Bitsy knew just the guy who could carry out this plan. She put a call into Snakeboots.

CHAPTER 24

Now that he had the go-ahead to implement the 4Rs of the Jedi mind trick, Snakeboots knew the first task was to find the right TV lawyer to represent Cricket Man. He or she would need three essential skills:

The ability to defend the indefensible

The ability to lie while looking straight at the camera

The ability to dispute any incriminating evidence against Cricket Man as deep state intervention in the judicial system

Finding this legal mouthpiece would not be a problem. Just watch CNN or Fox News long enough, she figured, and a star shyster would emerge.

Sure enough, there she was. Laetitia Poplar had, after the last election, formed an organization based on the premise "It is all a lie that the big lie is a lie," which challenged election results. The redundancy in the organization's mantra allowed her to attack any inconvenient truths as lies, perpetrated by the usual time-worn but effective attack on the lying fake media. She was a modern-day adherent to the doctrine of Joseph Goebbels, the infamous Nazi propagandist, who adhered to the doctrine that if you repeat a lie often enough, it becomes the truth.

Laetitia was a graduate of Frump University Online Law School. She declared herself as "The People's Lawyer" and a "Pit Bull with Lipstick," while emphasizing that she could go toe-to-toe with those bow-tie-wearing effete snobs from fancy East Coast law schools who, according to her, had never done a day's work in their lives. The fact that Frump Law School was an unaccredited money mill did not impede her ability to go on TV and espouse irrational and baseless legal theories. She argued common sense dictated that when her candidate lost, "everybody knew" there must have been election chicanery. She was a maestro of misinformation and half-truths in a skirt. She was perfect to defend Cricket Man.

Snakeboots decided to approach Laetitia by appealing to her sense of justice and her willingness to defend the little man against the powers that be. He described Cricket Man as a victim of powerful forces in the deep state determined to protect the status quo at any cost. They would use every resource they had to discredit him and everything he stood for. He would need someone like her, a judicial jackal, to fight the upcoming bare-knuckles fight on behalf of the working men and women of America. If she would give it her all, he would give her a hundred-thousand-dollar retainer upfront. "Now you are talking," she said. "Justice calls. Count me in."

Staging the first press conference with Laetitia and Cricket Man to address the fish-stuffing allegations was critical, since the visuals were as important as the words. They determined the ideal location was in front of a lug nut manufacturing company in Clayton, Georgia. Clayton was in the heart of fishing country and politically the strategic center of big lie territory. Local political leaders included a congressman who handed out AR-15 assault rifle lapel pins as a peace gesture and a local supervisor of elections who claimed Russian bots had taken over the last election for the board of education despite the fact that only paper ballots were used. The local newspaper had recently boasted that more citizens of Clayton had been arrested at the J6 Capitol riot than any other town of its size. The community would be a receptive audience for distortions and misinformation.

Cricket Man began the press conference by stating, unequivocally, that every allegation of Fishgate was untrue. They were simply the recriminations of a bitter former girlfriend looking for her piece of flesh. He had spent his life dedicated to creating equal-opportunity fishing, where everyone had a shot at the big prize. He then turned to the lug nut factory behind him and with an expression of total outraged sincerity proclaimed, "As to the charges I stuffed fish with lug nuts, I emphatically declare that I have never been in a lug nut factory, so help me God."

This was a riveting performance. The denial of an irrelevant fact about being in a lug nut factory had the audience totally confounded. It created the perfect segue for Laetitia to commence with a fifteen-minute rant attacking the deep state, Clinton operatives, TikTok, Hugo Chavez, and foreign software companies trying to illegally rig fishing tournaments. She then indignantly invoked unrelated constitutional articles and clauses, further befuddling those watching and listening. She had Sidney Powell of election conspiracy fame looking like a rank amateur in the big leagues of distortion and disinformation. The only thing she forgot to mention was Hunter Biden's laptop.

The next step in the Jedi mind trick is to invoke religion and redemption. The fact that you had denied doing what you now said was being absolved by the almighty was just a technical detail. Whether you had committed the offense or not was irrelevant. Pastoral redemption was available for all who had fallen by the wayside. If you had stayed on the straight and narrow, divine intervention was available as a hedge to forthcoming misdeeds, charges, and allegations. Kind of like a Catholic going to confession and saying, "I disobeyed my parents." It was all-inclusive and covered everything.

Securing a man or woman of the cloth to authenticate divine intervention was not a problem. Woke Diversification Identity Politics LLC, which had provided crowds for the Wienermobile, had a subsidiary, Bipartisan Heavenly Intervention Inc., which had a portfolio of ministers, rabbis, priests, mullahs, and other clerics available for "consulting and redemptive services." Perusing the list, Snakeboots quickly identified Pastor Bob of the Ministry of Faith Church in Eufaula, Alabama, as the most effective candidate to invoke heaven on behalf of Cricket Man.

After a brief conversation with Pastor Bob, Snakeboots knew he had the right man. The right reverend explained that "Who among us has not sinned?" was his standard opening line for those seeking redemption, and then he would fill in the blanks, depending on the transgression being absolved and the amount of the charitable contribution that was made to his church. If your contribution was sufficient for the premium package, your redemptive process might include the divining of snakes, speaking in tongues, and the investiture of spirits. Otherwise, the laying of hands and a few prayers would usually do it.

Snakeboots deferred on the premium package and went with the standard plus a slight surcharge for a press conference where "Who among us has not sinned?" would be followed by Pastor Bob chastising those who did not forgive the sins of others. At this point, there would be the laying of hands, whereupon Cricket Man would stand and proclaim that he had seen the light, fall to his knees, and claim he regretted his past misdeeds and would sin no more. The whole spiritual event would be over in minutes but could be circulated on YouTube, TikTok, and other social media to pave the way for the final 4R—the revival tour.

Pastor Bob was masterful, and it immediately resulted in positive political movement. Congressman Tanglewood and Congresswoman Sprout, who had previously announced they would return all campaign contributions associated with Cricket Man, both announced they had entered a period of reflection and reconsideration on their earlier decision. This was the beginning of the revival tour by political proxy. It was essentially third-party exoneration.

After exchanging phone calls, the two members of Congress issued a joint press release, invoking the refuge of bipartisanship and announcing they had determined it was in the national interest to retain the campaign contributions. Chairman Tanglewood went on to say who was he to judge and that God works in mysterious ways. Congresswoman Sprout expounded on the need to "accept a helping hand" when offered and that political contributions were just another form of "Manna from Heaven."

Implementation of the 4R Jedi mind trick seemed to be

working well enough to keep Cricket Man out of the slammer, but despite the statements of Tanglewood, Sprout, and others, his political standing was dubious. He clearly was damaged goods, and his ability to continue to front the consortium was questionable. Snakeboots was a firm believer in loyalty, but loyalty only went so far. The whole mess reminded him of George McGovern, who was a "1,000 percent" behind Senator Tom Eagleton as his running mate until he dumped him. Political expediency called out for a new strategy for the consortium. It was time to throw Cricket Man under the bus.

CHAPTER 25

The Sun Tzu shtick sold well with the clients, but now Snakeboots had to create a scheme to put Pop-Tarts into space. Time for some political rope-a-dope.

Substantively, there was little merit to putting Pop-Tarts on the space shuttle. There was, however, one little quirky aspect of astronaut food that provided a sliver of opportunity. Turns out bread was not available to our space pioneers for two reasons. First, it had a very short shelf life and was not suitable to be freeze-dried like many other food items. Secondly, bread constituted a unique safety hazard in that crumbs would float and clog air vents, which is not a good thing when you are miles up in space.

Why not have Pop-Tarts fill the bread void? Sure, it was a stretch, but Snakeboots had successfully pitched more outlandish notions. Overcoming the shelf-life issue was a no-brainer. Pop-Tarts were still good for months after the "Use By" date, and as a practical matter, with all the sugar and preservatives, they could go on a trip to the moon and back and still be edible for another crew on the next trip.

The crumbs floating in weightlessness issue was another matter. It might test food science credulity, but the argument could be that the jelly filling acted as a binding agent. Sort of the Elmer's glue of the food world. Maybe not the most appetizing analogy, but one the intended congressional audience could comprehend, and even though it was not probable, it was at least plausible, which is all that was necessary. Dubiety was not a disqualifier in political discourse when attempting to justify a preordained outcome.

To get this done, Snakeboots would kick what he dubbed the "pinball puzzle ploy" into gear, and he was the pinball wizard. He had four members of Congress to deal with, and only he would know all the pieces to the puzzle. The first two to deal with would be Girtz and Breen, who rode in the same clown car. Next would be Pendergast, whose feet never touched the ground. Finally, the Speaker, who considered all three of the aforementioned as major hemorrhoids in the legislative process. Snakeboots would bounce member to member like a pinball, sucking them into supporting certain positions while camouflaging the big picture of who was doing what to whom.

Congresswoman Breen had introduced her bill to make Pop-Tarts an item in the School Breakfast program with great fanfare. Fortuitously for Snakeboots, she referred to Pop-Tarts as "an American staple that serves as the glue keeping traditional families intact." This was a ludicrous statement that not surprisingly generated a response from Representative Pendergast, who charged her with encouraging children to eat glue and cited Consumer Product Safety Commission studies that glue consumption by children could be toxic and, even if not life-threatening, could result in severe constipation. Inflamed, Congresswoman Breen suggested that Representative Pendergast "glue her mouth shut for the sake of the country" while describing the congresswoman from Rhode Island as "a reptilian creature who periodically slithers out of the swamp."

The great glue debate was a godsend for Snakeboots.

The kerfuffle over glue would be a backdrop as he pinballed member to member. He would send them off in different directions without them knowing they were getting played. Actually, not too difficult of a task, considering the collective IQ of the three targets.

Representative Mickey Girtz was the easiest member of the trio to bamboozle. He was a politician with no bearings and hence no guardrails. His Pop-Tart legislation had been a ham-handed attempt to create defense bona fides where there were none. Moving him to some other phony position to fill the defense void would not be complicated. Girtz was malleable if he thought the focus was all about him and if it took care of his major political contributor, Thurston Reynolds IV.

Snakeboots arranged for a private meeting with Congressman Girtz at Bullfeathers, a popular watering hole for members of Congress and staff on Capitol Hill. Named Bullfeathers in recognition of President Teddy Roosevelt's favorite euphemism for bullshit, it was an appropriate location for a discussion between Snakeboots and the honorable congressman. Ensconced in a back booth, Snakeboots began his pitch by saying, "As you know," knowing full well that Mickey Girtz didn't know, but it played to his ego and was an opening to tell him what he didn't know and needed to know.

"As you know," Snakeboots began, "a secret arrangement has been reached for Pop-Tarts to be included as part of the meal plan on the next space shuttle mission. This will set the stage for it to become a staple of the newly created US Space Force. A development that will spike sales and exponentially exceed what inclusion in the meals-ready-to-eat

(MRE) program might have meant to category growth. Now, I am not at liberty to disclose further details, but it is imperative that you get out in front of this. You need to take ownership."

Mickey's head was spinning with all the angles and opportunities this information presented. Handling Thurston Reynolds IV was a no-brainer. He would call him with this top-secret information, knowing that he would immediately share it with his Vice-President of Sales and Vice-President of Operations so they could ramp up production of the aluminum foil wrappers for Pop-Tarts.

With the deployment of this new information, positioning himself as a strategic military thinker was simple enough. He would hire a couple of retired generals to create testimonials as to his "intuitive strategic analytical capabilities" while further identifying him as "the political forefather" of the US Space Force. No one would know or care that all this praise and recognition was a result of airmen eating Pop-Tarts. For those who wanted to know what all the fuss was about—Bieberites and Jerry Seinfeld fans— selective leaks to *People* magazine, *Hollywood Life*, and postings on TikTok and Facebook would do the job.

Mickey quickly deduced that this new space shuttle development was a total winner for him. It would dramatically increase his name recognition on the east coast of Florida, where the Kennedy Space Center was located, while drawing national attention to him as a defense thought leader. Not unimportantly it would also fill the coffers of his biggest supporter/contributor. He would get credit for everything while essentially doing nothing. He was very good at doing nothing, but as a transactional politician, he knew there was always a catch.

"What do you want from me?" he queried Snakeboots.

"Not much, just have Barb Breen sideline her School Breakfast legislation and keep her yap shut," answered Snakeboots.

"No problem," assured Mickey. "I will let her have first billing at the next Regulate Women's Bodies, Not Guns rally. She has been chomping at the bit for years to do that and will agree to just about anything for that opportunity."

Getting Representative Lizzie Pendergast to get off her sanctimonious high horse was a whole different undertaking. Snakeboots could tee up that Girtz's MRE legislation was dead and that Breen's school breakfast bill had died with it, but Pop-Tarts on the space shuttle was problematic. It wouldn't be enough for her to claim victory over Girtz and Breen. The space shuttle was too easy a target for her to spew righteous indignation from her moral high ground. He needed something that would cool her jets and make her think twice.

Once again, just like the ruckus over glue, what Snakeboots needed landed right in his lap. NASA announced with great fanfare that the next shuttle launch would be commanded by the first Native American female astronaut. This would be an event acclaimed by every Progressive as further evidence of the lofty goals of Indigenous people and the need for a total ban on the celebration of Thanksgiving Day. No conscientious liberal would do anything to detract from this historical event. Not even Lizzie Pendergast would have the political nerve to detract from this ballyhooed moment of political correctness.

During the Jack Abramoff Indian tribe lobbying scandal,

Snakeboots had gotten to know Abooksigun Kuman, who was Director of Casino Operations for the Narragansett Indian tribe in Rhode Island. Abooksigun had been an effective spokesperson for the Christian Coalition, which had him on retainer to speak out against allowing gambling by other tribes in other states. When asked if there wasn't an inherent contradiction between his job and his anti-gambling position, he deftly dodged the question by claiming, "It is better to keep crime concentrated in one area so you can keep an eye on it." His answer so flustered the congressman who asked it at the hearing that he had no comeback.

Snakeboots had a keen eye for talent when he saw it and over the past few years had allowed Abooksigun to use his Sea Island condominium, accompanied by his twenty-five-year-old female admin, for periods of "reflection and reconstitution." In the back of his mind, while making his beachfront condo available, he thought, *You never know when you might need a well-spoken Indian*, and now was the time for him to call in this chit.

He had a simple request of Abooksigun. Would he be willing to call Congresswoman Pendergast and explain the importance of Pop-Tarts on the space shuttle? He could explain that their presence was meant as an overture from Indigenous people to non-Indigenous people, to close the cultural gap between American Indians and the white man oppressor. It was critical that the positive energy created by this symbolic gesture not be dissipated by distractions. They needed her full support. Also, by the way, it wouldn't hurt if he let her know that the Narragansett tribe PAC had just voted to make another contribution to her campaign.

Abooksigun called Snakeboots back the next day to report his conversation with Congresswoman Pendergast had gone well. She recognized the cultural sensitivity of what he had described, and since she was not a member of the Science, Space, and Technology Committee, it would not be incumbent on her to say anything but that she supported "Indigenous people going airborne."

Snakeboots expressed his sincere thanks to Abooksigun. He went on to say what a dear friend he had been and to let him know that if there was anything he could do to reciprocate, just let him know and consider it done.

"You're welcome," responded Abooksigun. "By any chance, is your condo available on New Year's Eve?"

The pinball puzzle ploy was nicely coming together. Girtz, Breen, and Pendergast were simultaneously out spinning their wheels and going nowhere fast. Now all he had to do was convince the Speaker he could politically kneecap all three by putting Pop-Tarts on the space shuttle.

CHAPTER 26

The clock was ticking. Peter Pork and Molly Mustard had now been held captive for almost forty-eight hours, and according to the experts at Cornell, the next batch of 152 hot dogs would put them into hot dog revulsion syndrome. If this were to happen, hot dog sales would plummet, and any chance Bitsy had to become the permanent Executive Director of the National Hot Dog and Sausage Council would evaporate.

Bitsy texted Snakeboots with an urgent request to come to her office on K Street. He, at the time, was having an enjoyable lunch with a potential new client, the President of a recently formed advocacy group for the tobacco industry, Cigarettes Cut Health Care Costs, whose mantra was "Dead before Something Else Gets You." Already, three members of Congress had stopped by, offering, "Let me know how I can help." The timing of the text from Bitsy was somewhat irksome, coming as it did just as they were getting into the crème frappe dessert and the nitty-gritty of fees, but he excused himself, telling the potential client that Senator Schmuck needed him, and headed over to the Hot Dog Council office.

When he got to her office, she was reviewing old notes from her revisionist world history class on the art of negotiation. Bitsy reminded Snakeboots how Henry Kissinger had been a master at creating "back channels," whether it was opening China or ending the Vietnam War. If they could replicate his approach with the kidnappers, it might lead to a negotiated settlement with the ALF, the return of the two hot doggers and the Wienermobile, and possibly her being considered for the Nobel Peace Prize, like Dr. Kissinger. If they pulled this off, at a minimum, she would be the hands-down favorite to be selected as Woman of the Year by the National Barbeque and Grilling Association.

Snakeboots attentively listened as Bitsy implored him to create a back channel to the kidnappers in time to prevent Peter and Molly from having to ingest the third tranche of 152 hot dogs. He diplomatically didn't disagree with the approach but suggested it be accompanied by a surreptitious reconnaissance mission that would allow them to pinpoint the location of the hostages and prepare for an Entebbe-type raid if need be. It was critical that they be ready, should negotiations fail.

Charlie Harrison of the Food Marketing Institute (FMI) was the go-to guy to help Snakeboots establish a back channel. He suggested a grocery store produce section as a place where two celery stalks would be comfortable and not arouse suspicion. His plan was to contact the kidnappers through an ad in the classified section of the *Vegetarian Times*. The ad would direct "anyone holding a couple of hot doggers and their vehicle" to check out the okra section of the Safeway store on Capitol Hill for further instructions on "how to end this national nightmare peacefully and amiably." Charlie felt comfortable using the okra section, since it was a place that would go unnoticed for days, thereby significantly decreasing the likelihood of the note inadvertently going home with someone as part of a charcuterie board. Snakeboots liked what he was hearing and gave the mission the go-ahead.

The ransom note was placed under two-day-old okra as planned by a stock boy who was slipped five dollars to execute the drop-off. The note was a point-by-point rejoinder to the liberation front's demands. Bitsy insisted it be firm yet conciliatory while demonstrating the council was negotiating from a position of strength, which, as she had read in *The Art of the Deal*, was the sine qua non of any give and take.

The note read as follows:

Attention Animal Liberation Front Abductors: *In response to your ransom demands, we propose the following:*	
Personhood:	All animals will be given first and last names and will be allowed to use the farm address to set up individual Amazon accounts.
Freedom from Cruelty:	No animal family gatherings will be allowed over the holidays.
Preventive Health Care:	Each barn will be designated a Smoke-Free Zone. In addition, everyone qualifying as a senior will be provided a prescription for Prevagen for memory care.

No Factory Farming:	All facilities will be divided into condominiums with a tenant's Bill of Rights.
Freedom from Anxiety:	Valium will be readily available.
Pension Benefits:	Each animal condominium complex will have a pickleball court.
Collective Bargaining:	Condominium residents will be eligible to join the Amalgamated Meat Cutters of the United Food and Commercial Workers (UFCW) of the AFL-CIO.

Implementation of these commitments is dependent on the safe return of the two hot doggers and the Wienermobile. If you agree to these terms, leave a written response in the okra section of the Safeway on Capitol Hill. Failure to do so will have extreme repercussions.

Signed,
Bitsy Baskin
Executive Director in Extremis
National Hot Dog and Sausage Council

While the messaging through the back channel was underway, the implementation of Snakeboots's recommended ancillary reconnaissance mission was put into motion. The plan was both elaborate and simple.

When the celery stalks approached the vendor for the third batch of 152 hot dogs, they would be greeted by a poster announcing a one-time-only tie-in with DoorDash. Anyone who bought at least 152 hot dogs to be delivered by DoorDash at no cost would get two Tofurkey meatless hot dogs for free. The idea was that it would be impossible for two emaciated, starving vegans to refuse meatless hot dogs.

Turns out the two hostage holders had been surviving on seaweed sandwiches for the past few days, and the Tofurkey dogs would be a welcome change. In addition, they were comfortable with the DoorDash connection, since their ESG newsletter recently reported that the company had just committed to all-electric scooters by 2066 to combat climate change.

The two stalks gingerly approached the vendor, concerned that taking advantage of the one-day-only promotion might draw unwanted attention. Trying to appear nonchalant, the shorter stalk inquired as to the delivery range of the promotion and was informed by the vendor, "It's the continental United States as well as Guam and Puerto Rico." Assured that they qualified, the taller stalk proceeded to order seventy-six hot dogs with ketchup, seventy-six hot dogs with just mustard, and two Tofurkey dogs, one with sauerkraut and one with relish, to be delivered to the George Mason Memorial.

Both the vendor and the DoorDash person gave a quizzical look when he mentioned the George Mason Memorial. Neither one had a clue where it was, causing the vendor to ask, "Is that in the continental United States?"

The taller stalk assured them that it was. In fact, it was just a few hundred yards away, around the Tidal Basin near the Thomas Jefferson Memorial. "Just keep an eye out for a twenty-seven-foot hot dog vehicle, and that will be the spot."

Snakeboots had recruited the diminutive Holly Hawkins of the Consumer Brands Association to pose as the DoorDash delivery person. Her favorite color was red, which was in line with the DoorDash motif, and her gift for gab would allow her to talk her way out of a jam and escape should things get dicey. Holly, however, ever the crafty one, had an ulterior motive other than simply securing the release of the hostages. The notoriety that came with this daring escapade would vault her into the upper echelons of the women's movement. She would become a historical figure like Gloria Steinem, Bella Abzug, and Shirley Chisholm. This also was an opportunity to plant a feminist flag in the fight for consumerism and to show those anti-Pink Tax Progressive whining wimpettes what a real woman could do.

Holly, in a red jumpsuit and goggles, kickstarted her Vespa, the sidecar filled with the order, and started cruising around the Tidal Basin toward the Jefferson Memorial. Sure enough, just a few hundred yards down the road was a cul-de-sac in which two people were hog-tied to a statue with duct tape over their mouths, near a vehicle topped off with a mock hot dog. She whipped into the opening, where two celery stalks were seated behind a card table with a sign-up sheet for anyone interested in joining the Animal Liberation Front. The sign-up sheet was blank.

Trying to act nonplussed, Holly asked the two if they had ordered 152 hot dogs, seventy-six with ketchup and seventy-six with mustard, as well as two Tofurky meatless hot dogs, one with sauerkraut and the other with relish?

They gave her the thumbs-up and then instructed her to put the meat dogs in front of the two "writhing over there" and leave the Tofurkey with them on the table. Apologetically, the short stalk then commented, "We are a little short on cash for a tip, but hope this helps," and gave her a fifty-cent coupon for a Morningstar vegan frozen pizza.

Holly mounted her scooter and with a Jersey salute for being stiffed on the tip sped out of the cul-de-sac. She then backtracked on foot and hid behind the brown National Park Service sign identifying the site as the George Mason Memorial. From this vantage point, she was able to take numerous pictures of the hostage area, the two hot dog-gers, and most importantly the two kidnappers, who had removed the tops of their costumes in order to eat the Tofurkey dogs. It was a male and a female, a forlorn duo who could have served as poster children for a third-world relief fund.

Having accomplished her mission, Holly hurriedly went to join Snakeboots, Charlie Harrison of FMI, and Randy Lesher of AFB, who were already seated at the Palm restaurant for their weekly lunch. Arriving on her Vespa and wearing her red jumpsuit and goggles, she was accosted by the maître d', who wanted to know if she was there for a pickup and directed her to the delivery platform behind the kitchen. Indignantly, Holly told him to eff off and marched to the table where her three lobbyist colleagues were already on their second round of drinks.

Excitedly, after ordering a double Chardonnay, she began to recount her adventures of the day. Going to the hostage site, coolly and calmly making the delivery, circling back, and taking photos, including headshots of the two kidnappers. Surely, she mused, this would be worthy of an entire segment of *America's Most Wanted* with her in a starring role, not to mention her being nominated for inclusion in the Political Women's Hall of Fame.

As the phone photos were passed around the table, all admitted they had never seen that location before, and no one recognized the hostage takers. They all agreed they looked like anorexic, bedraggled hippies, but no one had an idea who they might be. Possibly the FBI database might be able to ID them. Snakeboots announced that he would forward the photos to the client and that they could congratulate themselves on a good day's work with another round of drinks.

Bitsy, back at the office, perused the photos but had to admit to herself she was none the wiser as to who these people were. She decided to forward them to Clyde, who was in a fugue state, laid out horizontally on the couch in the adjoining office. The staff had been directed not to disturb him, but she would periodically update him so he would think he was still in charge. Maybe something in the photo would trigger a memory in his addled brain.

It was a primal scream, the likes of which no one in the office had ever heard before. The front desk receptionist pushed the secret panic button under her desk, activating the building's armed security team. Bitsy dropped her iPhone midtext and bolted into the adjoining office, where Clyde Cartwright was upright on the couch with a look of horror on his face. He appeared close to entering into a catatonic state when he blurted out, "It is Stardust Magellan and Yardley Thomas" before collapsing back on the couch.

CHAPTER 27

The Lazarus-like political resurrection of Cricket Man was a masterpiece of diversion and deception executed by TV lawyer Laetitia Poplar and Pastor Bob. It exploited class warfare with all the Bannon-esque trappings. Whether it would be enough to make him a marketable item remained to be seen.

The PR spin masters worked the cable networks, Twitter, and other social media, portraying Cricket Man as a martyr, not a villain. Pastor Bob invoked every biblical fishing cliché as a rationale for forgiveness for the misdeeds Cricket Man never admitted doing. Faux lawyer Poplar, citing rulings from that esteemed jurist, Judge Judy, tried to flip the narrative by arguing that Cricket Man and his family were due compensatory and punitive damages for years of "rural neglect at the hands of the landed gentry of the ruling class" that resulted in his suffering from "dissociative disorders" including "depersonalization" and "derealization." In addition, to further confuse the issue, she warned that she was preparing a multimillion-dollar class action lawsuit on behalf of the lug nut industry for defamation and material misrepresentation. Her nonstop media blitz and baseless claims were taking gaslighting to a whole new level. The takeaway from all of this by the viewing public was total befuddlement and a massive outpouring of contributions to the Poplar Cricket Man Defense Fund and an overwhelming response to a GoFundMe request to further the biblical mission of Pastor Bob, requiring additional staff at his two 800-number call centers in Jakarta.

All of this media attention, however, had one significant political downside. It drew attention to the legislative sleight of hand Snakeboots had planned for funding the consortium. His idea had been to quietly slip a mere $5 million into the House omnibus appropriations bill. Sit silently as the House and Senate combined their massive spending bills and then watch it be signed into law as part of a gargantuan catch-all, must-pass piece of legislation.

The controversy over Cricket Man had raised the ire of zealots on the right and the left. Right-wingers questioned whether cricket farming was just another form of corporate welfare for Republicans in overalls. The left challenged that crickets were just mini-livestock requiring standardized regulations to assure their sentience and general well-being. Congressional district offices were being pummeled by the crazies from both sides. The madness even extended to saffron-robed Hare Krishnas releasing hundreds of crickets in congressional offices while staging sit-ins to protest the exploitation of what they deemed to be the chirping children of God. The issue had evolved into a political clusterfuck.

In addition, all of this commotion surrounding crickets was starting to spook Representative Sprout, who had introduced the National Cricket Consortium Act of 2023. Sure, she and her lobbyist benefactors knew it was a Trojan horse, but the public took it for real. Children were writing their congressional representatives, pleading with them not to do anything that would harm cute, friendly crickets. Each letter was accompanied by a sticker of Jiminy Cricket holding a stop sign. Cricket Wireless saw its stock plummet after the *Daily Beast* issued a news story with the headline "More Cricket Regulation on the Way."

Meanwhile, Ghann's Cricket Farm in Georgia saw a surge in sales after an internet rumor spread that after a ban on AR-17 rifles, crickets were next, a rumor that was exacerbated when Greg Gutfeld, while co-hosting *The Five* on Fox News, quipped, "After they take your guns, what is next, crickets?" Suffice it to say, the cricket political landscape was in free fall, and something dramatic would be necessary to pull it out of its nose dive, or all would be lost.

In a time of crisis, Snakeboots decided it was time to do what he did best, and that was to go to lunch. He gathered with his fellow foodies—Randy, Holly, and Charlie—to plot how they might salvage the Cricket Consortium. Once the perfunctory comments had been made that this was the most acrimonious congress ever and how difficult it would be to get anything done, Charlie, of the Food Marketing Institute, raised the ante. Turns out some of his member grocery stores were being vandalized by the saffron-robed Hare Krishnas, who had become aware of the institute's involvement with the Cricket Consortium legislation. Their tactic was to release crickets in the produce sections while chanting religious overtures and beating drums. Once they left, invariably patrons would hear shrieks from other customers as they discovered an infestation of crickets in the kale, broccoli, and carrots. His member companies were apoplectic, and his phone was ringing off the hook. People were demanding they do something to stop the madness in Washington.

After another round of drinks, the group knew what

must be done. The only way to salvage this fiasco and still make a few bucks was to call for a study, knowing full well that a study was the graveyard of the legislative process. Once completed, it would be something else to put in a filing cabinet, but if structured correctly, it would come with some dollars that could be plucked. Maybe not $5 million, but at least something for all of this time and effort.

It was Randy who spoke up first. "We can calm this whole ruckus down in short order if we can get Congresswoman Sprout to announce a study of the cricket crisis and say that she plans to hold her legislation in abeyance until a definitive study is completed. It will need to consist of a blue-ribbon committee with staff and outside counsel. We leave the deadline for the final report open-ended so it can quietly fade away as interest in the issue dissipates with a fresh news cycle."

"I love it," chimed in Charlie. "This will get Sprout off the hook and allow me to tell my member grocery stores that we have put the kibosh on this whole controversy."

Snakeboots also liked what he was hearing. Time to throw Cricket Man under the bus and make sure they all got out of this with something. Hell, he wasn't getting paid anything upfront for all of this anyways, and a little back-end remuneration would make it all worthwhile.

The conversation with Representative Sprout was a no-brainer. She agreed with Snakeboots that it was time for an orderly retreat and that a call to the secretary of agriculture to create a cricket commission using discretionary funds was in order.

She placed the call a week before the Appropriations Subcommittee was to consider the Ag Department's annual funding bill. The secretary found the idea to have great merit, especially after he was told that the Executive Director of the commission would be Trip Tanglewood, the wayward son of Chairman Tanglewood. The creation of a blue-ribbon committee was always an attractive proposition. It would allow him to reward the party faithful with meaningless positions and titles as members of the committee. Plus, the ability to select outside counsel was an opportunity to financially reward administration stalwarts, knowing full well that half of the funds would be recycled back to the campaign committee in the form of contributions.

Following her discussion with the secretary, Representative Sprout called her consortium co-sponsors, Congressman Buzz Orkin and Congressman Raji Nehru, to see if they might join her and the secretary at a press conference to announce the establishment of the committee. Congressman Orkin was inclined to participate but asked, "What is a blue-ribbon committee?" to which she replied, "It is different than a red, green, or pink commission." He thought this made perfect sense and told her to count him in. Representative Nehru was less probing. He just wanted to know if there would be cameras and, when assured there would be, responded, "Cricket is my favorite sport. I will be there."

The press conference to announce the formation of the National Cricket Commission under the auspices of the United States Department of Agriculture was held in the foyer of the Cannon House Office Building. Standing behind a bank of microphones was Tom Saysack, secretary of Agriculture, and the Honorable Lucy Sprout. They were flanked on both sides by Congressman

Buzz Orkin and Congressman Raji Nehru.

Congresswoman Sprout initiated the proceedings by thanking everyone for being there and modestly admitting that when she introduced H.R. 1776, the National Cricket Consortium Act of 2023, she had never anticipated the firestorm of interest and activity that would follow. She then proudly proclaimed, "The role of crickets in our national food supply and their impact on the fishing industry is a discussion we must and will have. It will require a national conversation, engaging some of our country's best minds from business, labor, faith-based institutions, and academia. To that end, we are gathered here today." She then asked her two colleagues if they would like to say anything before she introduced the secretary.

Congressman Orkin took the mic and with the perfunctory "I will be brief" and thanked Congresswoman Sprout and Secretary Saysack for their "leadership on this issue." He then, with dramatic gravitas, went on to state, "What we do here today will have a profound impact on the lives of trillions of bugs. I cannot overstate its importance."

Following Representative Orkin, Congressman Nehru thanked the media for covering this "august occasion." He then went on to remark, "As a young boy watching cricket, never in my wildest imagination did I ever dream that I would be here today helping form a national commission on cricket. Thank you, America, where anything is possible."

It was then the turn of Secretary Saysack to announce the creation of the National Cricket Commission. The charter of the commission was to study the impact of crickets on our "food supply, farming, fishing, rural development, national security, pest control, and other matters that might come before the commission." He then went on to announce that this undertaking would be under the direction of a blue-ribbon panel comprised of:

- Holly Hawkins of the Consumer Brands Association (CBA)
- Randy Lesher of the American Farm Bureau (AFB)
- Charlie Harrison from the Food Marketing Institute (FMI)
- Jack Hook, Director of the National Fishing Federation (NFF)
- Mickey Frost, representing the American Pest Control Association (APCA)
- Juanita Alvarez, CEO of Orkin
- Govinda Chander of the International Society for Krishna Consciousness (ISKC)
- John Brown, President of the Amalgamated Brotherhood of Varmint and Bug Eradication (AFL-CIO)

The secretary went on to say how much he appreciated their willingness to serve, and in recognition of the burden it would place on their busy schedules, they would be compensated on a per diem basis. He then announced how excited he was that Trip Tanglewood of North Dakota had agreed to relinquish his current responsibilities as Director of Logistics for one of DC's major legal entities and serve as Executive Director. According to the secretary, Trip was uniquely qualified for the position, having been a member of 4-H in high school. He was also an avid fisherman and enjoyed exotic cuisine. Finally, he added, almost as a footnote, that the commission would have the support of outside counsel from the prestigious law firm of P. J. "Snakeboots" Jackson, who had agreed to serve with a modest retainer.

CHAPTER 28

The interplay of Representative Girtz, Breen, and Pendergast was a slapstick comedy routine that made the Keystone Cops look like a military drill team. There was a reason the trio's sobriquet was the Clown Caucus. Amid all this comedy, Snakeboots's pinball puzzle ploy was falling nicely into place.

The verbal barbs between Breen and Pendergast over the glue and Pop-Tarts was a political catfight that was garnering national attention. In a diatribe of incoherent word salad, Representative Pendergast accused Congresswoman Breen of being a "feckless shill for the food industry turning our children into economic missiles aimed at their mother's pocketbooks." Breen responded by slamming Pendergast as a "gaseous blowhard" emitting more climate-changing methane than Elsie the Cow on Elmer's Glue, and if she was serious about her professed concern for the environment, she would "lower the methane output by keeping her yap shut." The spat drew the attention of *Saturday Night Live*, which did a segment mocking Elmer's glue as a substitute for Pepto-Bismol when children suffered from diarrhea, indigestion, and stomach cramps. The episode resulted in spiked sales of Elmer's glue and the company having to issue a statement warning that glue consumption was ill-advised and might cause "constipation and irregular bowel movements."

Meanwhile, as expected, Mickey Girtz had leaked the possibility of Pop-Tarts on the space shuttle to his buddy Thurston Reynolds IV, emphasizing that this info was highly confidential and not to be shared with anyone, a stipulation that ensured Thurston would immediately divulge it to numerous business associates so that they could prepare for a windfall of new orders. One of the associates was the company's Vice-President of Investor Relations, who briefed stock analysts to expect sales to be "over the moon," resulting in the stock price tripling in value.

Girtz, as planned, then set about to establish himself as a far-sighted military strategist. He contacted a company called Beltway Bandits Inc., which advertised itself as having a bevy of retired generals, admirals, and other high-ranking military officials media trained and on call to corroborate, defend, and/or promote any and all issues related to defense and the armed forces. Here he found a retired former Air Force general who had categorized former Air Force general Curtis LeMay as a "wimp" and said that his Vietnam War threat to "bomb 'em back to the stone age" was simply "pussyfooting around" and another indication the military had gone woke. Congressman Girtz knew this was his man, so he put him on a retainer with the assignment to hit the talk shows and cable networks to posit the notion that the key to the Space Force was its food supply. His argument was simple. "How long can a suborbital or intergalactic space flight last? As long as they have food." He would then allude to the work of Congressman Girtz, who he would identify as a "strategic thinker" and "military innovator" for his foresight regarding the critical nexus between food supply and space flight.

Snakeboots, seeing all this unfold, sensed the time was right to approach Speaker McCrudy about Pop-Tarts on the space shuttle. The Speaker was unaware of the strategic leak to Girtz and thought the rookie congressman was still focused on his legislation to get Pop-Tarts included in the MRE program. He also assumed McCrudy was watching with glee as Breen and Pendergast pummeled each other over glue and Pop-Tarts. It was time to execute the last and most critical element of the puzzle ploy.

Speaker McCrudy was a malleable political amoeba. His rise to Speaker was the manifestation of the Peter Principle, where one rises to his or her level of respective incompetence. He thrived on being called Mr. Speaker, relished its trappings, and was easily manipulated by people playing to his ego. Easy prey for Snakeboots. Manipulating political egos was one of his strong suits.

The ornate Speaker's office in the Capitol is fertile ground for a lobbyist. Whoever sits behind the desk in that office basks in power and is always anxious to demonstrate that she or he has it. Getting into the office was half the battle for most lobbyists, but not for Snakeboots, who had spent a career doling out campaign cash on both sides of the aisle. Asked one time about a change in power in the House from Democrat to Republican, he quipped, quoting President Lyndon Johnson when asked the shape of the world, "Flat or round, I can teach it either way." Politicians were simply pieces on a chessboard to be played accordingly. Snakeboots had access, hence power, and he knew how to use it.

"Mr. Speaker, your tenure reminds me of the late, great Speaker of the House Sam Rayburn, and your legacy will be equally illustrious. As you know, his famous adage was 'To get along, go along,' or there will be consequences. I am afraid, however, some of the younger members, specifically Girtz, Breen, and Pendergast, seem oblivious to this unwritten rule. It may be time for you to teach them a lesson," advised Snakeboots.

"Thanks for putting me in the same class as Sam Rayburn. He is one of my heroes. He also used to run what was euphemistically referred to as 'the board of education,' where recalcitrant lawmakers would be called in to be read the riot act and explained the consequences of their failure to fall in line. Maybe that is what I need to do with our wayward trio," responded Speaker McCrudy.

"That might work, but maybe a public flogging could be as effective and also gain some political points for your party before the upcoming midterms," suggested Snakeboots.

"You got my attention. Keep going," answered McCrudy.

"How about you arrange to have Pop-Tarts on the next space shuttle? It is something only you can do. In one fell swoop, you undercut those three pains in the ass. Girtz looks like a fool pushing MRE legislation when Pop-Tarts are already rocketing toward the moon as part of the Space Force. Breen comes across as an outdated frump, talking about something as mundane as school breakfast. Finally, you will accomplish the impossible by forcing Pendergast to keep her mouth shut. She will be checkmated by the presence of a Native American astronaut on the next flight and will not say anything to detract from that mission. You accomplish all of this while ingratiating yourself and your party with millennials and Gen 2, not to mention Bieberites and Seinfeld fans, as a hip, with-it Speaker. All pluses and no minuses," explained Snakeboots.

"Damn, this sounds pretty good. How do you suggest that I go about all of this?" asked the Speaker.

"Actually, it is quite simple. Just put in a call to the Director of NASA. Their appropriations will be part of the omnibus, and it will not be lost on him as a former member of Congress that your support will be critical to get the funding they have requested. All he has to do is grant one simple favor and their budget request sails through," advised Snakeboots.

"I like it. Those three newbies need to understand this is the big league and I play hardball," reacted the Speaker before yelling out to his admin, "Matilda, get the Director of NASA on the phone."

CHAPTER 29

The shock to the system of Clyde Cartwright when he recognized the kidnappers as his nemeses, Stardust Magellan and Yardley Thomas, sent him into an unresponsive state of akinetic catatonia, a condition that prompted Bitsy to notify the board that she would continue to manage the day-to-day activities of the council until Mr. Cartwright was compos mentis.

Using the produce stock boy once again as the emissary, although he'd raised his rate to ten dollars, a counterproposal to the kidnappers' demands was placed in the Safeway store okra bin, and video cameras confirmed it had been picked up by two celery stalks. Now Bitsy and Snakeboots had to bide their time and wait for a response.

The fact that Clyde had blurted out the names of the two kidnappers before collapsing was a significant development. Accessing the Department of Homeland Security database, they were able to ascertain that the two were on the Vegan Terrorist Watch List and that they had been involved in numerous subversive, underground activities, including defacing a Piggly Wiggly storefront, TP'ing the front yard of the President of the American Meat Institute, and staging a sit-in at the main processing plant of the New Mexico Beef Jerky Company. The department described them as having undertaken these activities while operating in a "cannabis-induced fog of revolutionary zeal." The report went on to describe them as "unhinged sad sack insurgents" known to suffer from a "constant state of insatiable munchies with a strong predisposition for Little Debbie Frosted Fudge Cakes."

As Bitsy and Snakeboots reviewed the report, they were becoming increasingly concerned that the deadline for action was fast approaching. If Peter and Molly were forced to consume the third tranche of hot dogs, they were almost certain to enter into a state of hot dog revulsion syndrome, with all the dire consequences of that condition. It would become a media sensation, tank hot dog sales, and ruin any chance Bitsy would have at becoming the permanent Executive Director of the council.

Exercising extreme caution so as not to cause alarm, Bitsy told the receptionist to hold all calls, informing whoever called that she was in confidential discussions affecting the entire industry and could not be disturbed. Ensconced with Snakeboots in the council boardroom, she took out a whiteboard to detail the situation and to establish talking points for the development of an action plan. Her synopsis of the situation was as follows:

Two hot doggers and the Wienermobile were being held hostage.

They were being held in a nondescript cul-de-sac on the National Mall.

A ransom note had been received and a counteroffer delivered.

No response to the counter had been received.

The celery stalk kidnappers had been confirmed to be vegan terrorists Stardust Magellan and Yardley Thomas.

The two terrorists were essentially dimwits whose brains had been addled by years of illicit drugs.

According to the analysis by Homeland Security, they were in a constant state of marijuana-induced munchies and had an insatiable craving for Little Debbie Frosted Fudge Cakes.

Following the whiteboard presentation, Bitsy and Snakeboots began reviewing clips of the recent prisoner exchange of American basketball star Brittney Griner and Russian arms dealer Viktor Bout, the "merchant of death." They saw a lot of similarities between what had gone down with these two and what they were trying to do. Both agreed it could serve as a template for how to execute the release. One small problem: What did they have to offer without succumbing to a list of demands? Bitsy remembered from her freshman world affairs class that it was critical to pretend to never negotiate with terrorists. What would constitute an offer the hijackers couldn't refuse, yet make it look like the council had not succumbed to their demands?

Finally, it dawned on Snakeboots. Little Debbie Frosted Fudge Cakes. The stoned kidnappers had been holed up for almost forty-eight hours, and whatever snacks they had on hand must be gone by now. How about a trade for the two hog doggers and the Wienermobile for a van filled with fudge cakes and guaranteed safe passage? No concessions would be needed. The bait would be irresistible.

Bitsy loved it. Pulling this off would make her a historical Washington figure. She envisioned a movie along the lines of *All the President's Men*, the one in which Robert Redford and Dustin Hoffman sent secret messages and held clandestine meetings while dashing about with iconic Washington scenes in the background. Maybe Jennifer Aniston would play her in this surefire blockbuster. This was her opportunity for fame and Hollywood stardom. It was not time to be timid. "Let's go for it!" she screamed.

Snakeboots proceeded to lay out the plan. They would take out an ad in the personals section of the *Vegan Times* addressed to celery stalks but making sure not to disclose they knew their true identity. The ad would state simply, "Craving Little Debbies? A surprise awaits you in the okra section of your local Safeway." Cognizant of the law of supply and demand, the produce stock boy, who was an economics major at Georgetown University, increased the charge for placing the note in the okra section from ten to fifteen dollars. The note read as follows:

Celery Stalks,

In exchange for the safe return of the hot doggers and the Wienermobile, we are prepared to provide you with a 1972 VW van filled with Little Debbie Frosted Fudge Cakes and equipped with an eight-track tape player. If you agree with these terms, place a Brussels sprout in the frozen organic section. Details for the handoff will follow within twelve hours back in this okra bin.

Sure enough, video cameras caught two celery stalks trying to act inconspicuously, rummaging through the okra bin, retrieving the note, and retreating to the parking lot. Shortly thereafter, while one stood watch outside, the smaller stalk reentered the store, picked out a Brussels sprout, and placed it in the frozen organic section on top of a box of Green Giant peas. Game on.

The following day, after the produce stocker raised his fee again and demanded twenty dollars, another note was left in the okra bin. This note read:

> Celery Stalks,
>
> Rendezvous tonight at 2:00 a.m. on the steps of the Jefferson Memorial. Park the Wienermobile with the two hot doggers on the east side. The fudge-filled van will be parked on the west side. Look for someone wearing an Uncle Sam hat. If he says, "Hot dog," you reply, "Relish," thereupon we will exchange keys, and you can be on your way. If you agree with these swap arrangements, place two Brussels sprouts in the frozen organic section.

It was an instant replay of the other day. The kidnapping duo strolled into the store, found the note, and after a brief discussion in the parking lot, the smaller of the duo put two Brussels sprouts in the frozen organic compartment, only this time next to a bag of Bird's Eye broccoli florets.

Trip Tanglewood had never driven a stick shift before, and his halting attempt to maneuver the 1972 VW van evidenced that. Bitsy and Snakeboots had him dressed as a 1960s hippie with bell-bottom pants, a tie-dyed T-shirt, and an Uncle Sam hat so as to make him look like someone who would be driving a vintage 1972 party wagon. He arrived at the west side of the Jefferson Memorial right on time, carrying a roadie from Clyde's Bar and Grill in Georgetown. Unbeknownst to his two employers, Trip had spent the last few hours hitting the bar scene in Georgetown. Two sheets to the wind, at his last stop at Clyde's, he met four female legislative aides, who lived together on Capitol Hill. After securing their address and phone numbers, he boasted, "With any luck tonight, I will be by your place with the biggest damn wiener you have ever seen." A boast met with extreme skepticism and quickly discounted as simply whiskey talk.

Yardley and Stardust were relieved that this was almost over. Their supply of weed was just about out, and they hadn't had a decent snack in days. The idea of heading west with a van loaded with Little Debbie Frosted Fudge Cakes raised the specter of a whole new beginning. Stardust had read on her favorite app, the Cannabis Connection, that cheap land was available in southern Colorado, where you could "grow your own" and "co-exist with nature" while "communing with fellow weed warriors." It sounded like the Promised Land for two listless laggards.

They had to be smart about transporting Molly and Peter and decided the best approach would be to duct tape them on the back bumper of the Wienermobile under the arching end of the hot dog. Placing them undercover at the end of the wiener would decrease the odds of them being spotted and arousing undue suspicion. After rolling a couple of joints, they placed their bong between them in the front seat along with a Radio Flyer Red Wagon they used to transport it and other sundry drug paraphernalia. They then set out for the agreed-upon rendezvous spot and what the two flaming fantasists thought would be a new beginning.

All looked copacetic as the two hostage takers pulled up on the east side of the Jefferson Memorial. Unloading the wagon, they placed the bong on it, along with some rolling papers, a hookah, a lighter, a rolling machine, and a roach clip, and pulled it nonchalantly in front of the majestic memorial. The only person in sight was a homeless-looking fellow sitting on the steps in an Uncle Sam hat nursing a roadie.

Trip, who was totally buzzed, quickly deduced that since these were the only two celery stalks he had seen all night that these might be the hostage takers. They were pulling a Radio Flyer Red Wagon with a tall glass cylindrical object in it and seemed to be enveloped in smoke. All rather strange, but according to plan.

As they passed by, Trip, in a stage whisper, said, "Hot dog," causing the twosome to stop and respond, "Relish." He then, as a gesture of goodwill, handed them his roadie, from which both took a gulp, and they then returned the gesture by passing him a joint, from which he took two hits. They exchanged keys and, with a nod, departed in opposite directions. So far, so good.

Yardley and Stardust couldn't believe their eyes. The VW van was absolutely crammed full of Little Debbie Frosted Fudge Cakes, and to top it off, each package had a fifty-cent-off coupon for the next purchase. After surveying the scene, they decided to ditch the celery costumes so as not to make them so easily identifiable. The plan was to head south on I-95, turn west on the Beltway, and then peel off after the first couple of exits and continue west toward the promised land of Colorado. According to Google Maps, the drive would take twenty-four hours and twenty-four minutes.

After a couple of hours on the road, Yardley and Stardust realized they had seen the *Welcome to Maryland* sign three times. It then dawned on Stardust in their stoned stupor that they had been going in circles around the Washington Beltway for the entire time. Ever the intrepid travelers, they pulled into a Buc-ees truck stop, where they figured they would blend in with the other customers, who made the people of Walmart look upscale. They parked in the back, lit another joint, and using an old AAA map figured out which exit would take them to Route 66, and then on to Colorado. As focused as they were ever going to be, they cranked up the van, put in the only eight-track tape they had, which was, "In-A-Gadda-Da-Vida" by Iron Butterfly, and set out for a new life out west. Upon arrival, they planned to contact Google Maps and suggest that they recompute the driving time to Colorado to include two hours of Beltway diversion time.

Meanwhile, Trip, stoned and drunk, ambled over to the Wienermobile and pulled out the address of the four female Hill staffers he had met earlier that evening. At the time, it seemed to make perfect sense to hold off making contact with Snakeboots and Bitsy so he could swing by the ladies' residence and impress them with the promised longest wiener they would ever see.

Surveying the Wienermobile, Trip mulled over what to do with Molly and Peter strapped to the back. He had always been taught that it was rude to bring someone to a party who had not been invited, so having them join him when he visited the young ladies was out of the question. He also noticed there were only two seatbelts in the cabin of the vehicle, so it would be unsafe to have all three of them sit in the front. He took note that, other than some squirming and guttural sounds from their duct-taped mouths, they seemed quite comfortable. What the hell, he thought, why not just leave them where they were? What was a couple of more hours? It all made perfect sense to him.

It was 3:30 a.m. and still no word from Trip. Bitsy and Snakeboots were getting frantic that maybe the exchange had gone south and Trip was now being held captive. How in the world would Bitsy explain this to the board? What about the movie starring Jennifer Aniston? How would Snakeboots tell the chairman of the Ag Appropriations Subcommittee his son was being held hostage by vegan terrorists?

Desperate, there was only one thing left to do: call the DC Metropolitan Police and see if by chance they had come across the Wienermobile, a hippie dressed like Uncle Sam, or two vegans masquerading as celery stalks.

Miraculously, a couple of hours after the call, a squad car on routine patrol came across a vehicle double-parked on Capitol Hill with two individuals strapped and gagged on the back bumper. The officer, sensing something was not quite normal, knocked on the front door of the residence. It was answered by a twenty-something-year-old young lady. He asked her if she might know the owner of the giant hot dog vehicle out front. She pointed at a guy in bell bottoms and wearing an Uncle Sam's hat who was passed out on the couch. Then the officer asked what was his name, and she replied, "I have no idea, but he does have the biggest wiener we have ever seen."

CHAPTER 30

The 118th Congress, like all Congresses before it, started with lofty expectations and calls for bipartisanship, comity, civility, and reform. Every opening day speech declared it was time for the people's house to do the people's business without regard to party or political persuasion. Like all Congresses before it, none of this happened.

The past year had been marked by bitter infighting, name-calling, and personal attacks that exceeded the basest expectations. The debate over the final passage of the omnibus appropriations bill sent cable news ratings soaring as the demagoguery and vitriol reached new heights. Barb Breen described her colleague, Congresswoman Lucy Sprout, as nothing more than a "trailer park hood rat," to which Sprout responded by calling Breen a "shameless hussy" acting under the spell of a "tantric sex guru." Although no one knew what a "tantric sex guru" was, everybody assumed it was bad and categorized the back-and-forth as simply a catfight between two fundamentally maladjusted human beings.

It wasn't just the ladies going at it. Representative Girtz, never able to stay out of the spotlight, jumped into the fray by calling Congresswoman Pendergast a "human political weather vane" who simply parroted the latest woke cause as leader of the swamp cartel. Not to be outdone, Pendergast fired back that Girtz was an "amoral amoeba" who was the product of a "defective gene sequence" and whose mental acumen was one brick short of a load.

No such thing as decorum existed in the House of Representatives. Chaos was the new normal order. What was actually in the bill was irrelevant to all the theatrics underway. The only thing that really mattered was getting air time on cable news, and members of Congress did that by creating controversy where none existed. Everybody knew the game and that the bill would pass regardless of the content, so why not make some political hay?

Just as Snakeboots had predicted, none of the regular twelve appropriation bills had passed, forcing the House and Senate to consolidate them into a four-thousand-page, $1.7 trillion budget-busting omnibus bill. The whole thing was cobbled together in less than forty-eight hours, so no one really had a clue what was in it other than it had enough pork to feed a nation. Lobbyists swarmed the halls, pigeon-holing legislators, trying to make sure there was some aspect of this legislative tome that would allow them to declare victory. Some would get a full slab of bacon while others would get bacon bits, but everybody would get something.

Snakeboots had enough in the omnibus package to placate the clients and make him a few bucks. None of them really won, but they didn't lose, which was gold for a lobbyist, since they would come back to fight again another day. For a fee, of course.

The $27 billion Ag Approps section had three provisions that were the result of Snakeboots's handiwork.

Funding was provided for the establishment of a National Cricket Commission under the auspices of a blue-ribbon panel comprised of representatives of the food, labor, business, farming, faith-based institutions, and the fishing sectors. Panel members would be compensated on a per diem basis and be supported by a full-time Executive Director, outside counsel, and support staff. The panel was empowered to issue a "white paper" on the role of crickets in "food supply, national security, fishing, and any other area deemed relevant and essential."

Also included in the bill, in another section, were monies to conduct an assessment of "grain-based, fruit-filled aluminum-foil-packaged food items" in the space program and their impact on Native American astronauts. This study was precipitated by the scuttling of the last space shuttle launch with the first Native American astronaut. Turns out breadcrumb-like substances were found in the air vents before liftoff, causing NASA to abort the mission at a cost to the taxpayers of $14 million. The inspector general of NASA had requested the funds to launch an investigation into how this all happened and what quality controls might be necessary in the future to prevent alien objects from entering the space capsule ventilation system.

Finally, there was one last item having to do with hot dogs. The legislation noted that Americans spend approximately $7 billion a year on hot dogs and sausages yet these items had never received their due recognition as a mainstay of the American diet. Therefore, in order to ameliorate this oversight, the bill funded the creation of the Swine Institute within the Department of Agriculture. The institute was charged with bringing recognition to the role of the hot dog as a cultural icon in America and to serve as an advocate on behalf of all the pigs that made this possible.

Passage of the Omnibus Appropriations Bill went pretty well, true to form. Political posturing within a vacuum of information was shameless. Proponents of the bill declared it as an elixir for every ill facing the country. This bill, they claimed, would eliminate the national debt, prevent climate change, cure COVID, and restore America as the leader of the free world. On the other hand, opponents predicted imminent doom and dire consequences upon passage, including the abolition of social security and Medicare, the creation of food deserts, global instability, a return to the gold standard, and massive debt being thrust upon our children and grandchildren.

It was all theater anyways, since everybody knew it would eventually pass and all would be forgotten with the next news cycle. Members of the House and Senate had planes to catch, and hell if a mere $1.7 trillion to keep the government functioning was going to get in the way. It was also a matter of priorities. Most of them had fundraisers scheduled back in their districts, which clearly outweighed concern over some pesky provisions in a funding bill. Besides, the holidays were coming, which always provided a built-in excuse for having to leave town by referencing that well-worn rationale of the importance of family time. Time to call it quits, go home, and adjourn. Sine die.

CHAPTER 31

Elections have consequences, and the consequences for the country after the elections for the 119th Congress were not good. Mickey Girtz, Lizzie Pendergast, Lucy Sprout, and Barb Breen were all re-elected for another term. Like most members of Congress, this was the best job they ever had or would have, and they would do anything to keep it. They had a death grip on the government tit, and by God, they weren't going to let go. There was one bright spot in that Speaker McCrudy was defeated.

Relying on the collective amnesia of the American public, the campaign ads of Girtz, Pendergast, Sprout, and Breen created narratives devoid of reality.

Mickey Girtz made former Congressman George Sandoz look like a piker by taking embellishment to a new level. He appeared in a space suit next to a launchpad at Cape Kennedy, claiming to be the forefather of the US Space Force. The sheer audacity of the claim was breathtaking enough, but the ad then went on to include a testimonial from Thurston Reynolds IV, crediting Girtz with creating thousands of small-business jobs in the high-tech aluminum foil industry through his involvement with the Space Force.

Congresswoman Lucy Sprout's ads for re-election cited her role in the agriculture community when tomato growers were attacked and their livelihoods threatened. The visuals showed her handpicking tomatoes in a vast field among smiling migrant workers and then enjoying bowls of Campbell's tomato soup with the same workers while a mariachi band played in the background. According to her ads, the tomato industry would cease to exist without her, and the tagline directed viewers to "Think Sprout next time you eat a soup and salad."

Lizzie Pendergast positioned herself as a woke warrior, fighting against childhood obesity and willing to take on big food companies, whom she charged used our kids as "heat-seeking missiles zeroed in on their parents' wallets." Her TV spots included two animal rights activists, Yardley Thomas and Stardust Magellan, who credited her with the creation of the Swine Institute, where pig-raising ethics and working conditions for farm animals could be addressed. She also promised that, if re-elected, she would work to create an Indigenous people's hub in the Department of Health and Human Services, where methods of healing could be developed for traumatized, marginalized, and displaced persons while studying reparations for indigenous Alaskans and the elimination of Thanksgiving Day.

Finally, Barb Breen cast herself as a "cultural crusader with compassion" and declared that bleeding-heart liberalism was dead on arrival in her office. She further explained that the enemy party was not as feckless as they seemed to be and that she was starting the MAHA movement to "Make America Homogenous Again," to help real Americans fend off the threats to their way of life by the global elites. The platform of the MAHA movement called for a national divorce, in which red states separated from the blue, except for those portions of California where the Nixon and Reagan Presidential Libraries are located.

Speaker McCrudy was blindsided in his re-election campaign and went down in defeat. His opponent, a twenty-three-year-old ageism studies major, campaigned against him as a gaffer who believed in the Great Replacement Theory and as such should be replaced. The fact that the Speaker had not been back in his congressional district for over a year and had married a twenty-nine-year-old lobbyist for the Distilled Spirits Council seemed to have an unsettling impact on his constituents, which in turn may have had something to do with his defeat. After losing his seat, he became President of the Hibernian Irish American Society, an organization funded by the Potato Institute and Guinness and seeking an expansion of St. Patrick's Day into a weeklong celebration of Irish drink and food in recognition of the success of Irish Americans in overcoming bigotry and discrimination.

The period between an election and a new Congress is what lobbyists refer to as "the client carousel." Washington types who yearn to be near power never leave, but they do migrate from company to company, and among trade associations, think tanks, and advocacy groups. When they do, relationships and allegiances shift, and they often become new clients, but alas sometimes they end up as former clients.

Annika Svensson had exhausted her stint at Kellogg after running roughshod over anyone not in the pecking order above her. Generally despised by everyone who worked with and for her, she jumped at the chance to become Senior Vice-President at Hormel in charge of the so-called miracle meat, Spam. The press release announcing her appointment emphasized her interest in "continuing the nutritional contribution of Spam to the American diet since its introduction in 1937" and that the family-friendly culture of Hormel was ideally suited for her aspirations to create a caring, stress-free work environment filled with mutual respect and courtesy. The release concluded by her referencing her vision for the product to one day become an integral part of the School Lunch program and a substitute for chipped beef on toast in the military.

Not everyone shifted seamlessly from job to job. The Fishgate scandal, despite the best efforts of Pastor Bob and Laetitia Poplar, had made Rod McDonell radioactive. Not even the National Cricket Commission would touch him. He returned to his hometown of Dillard in North Georgia, where he opened a bait shop, promoting "Bugs they can't resist." He also became somewhat of a local celebrity, appearing on a late-night infomercial, pitching a new book, *What Is Fishy in Washington*, that was loosely based on his personal story of fame, failure, and redemption. It ended with someone asking his advice to young people going to Washington, to which he responded, "Don't."

During the transition between Congresses, the Hot Dog and Sausage Council announced significant management changes. Crediting Bitsy Baskin with having increased sales, expanding category recognition, and creating the Swine Institute while serving as Executive Director in Extremis, the board promoted the twenty-three-year-old wunderkind to full-time Executive Director. In addition, the board announced the appointment of two recent inductees into the Hot Dogger Hall of Fame, Peter Pork and Molly

Mustard, as "Tubular Steak Ambassadors for Buzz, Social Media, and Alchemy," a title that was totally incoherent to the board, but insisted upon by Bitsy as a way to make the organization relevant.

Subsequent to the announcements about Bitsy, Peter, and Molly, the council tweeted that Clyde Cartwright had been awarded a gold watch for his dedicated years of service and was retiring to the Villages in Florida after being diagnosed with neurasthenia.

After appearing in the Lizzie Pendergast ads, the Oscar Mayer Company decided not to press charges against Stardust Magellan and Yardley Thomas so as not to alienate "alternative food aficionados." Deciding to get while the getting was good, the two decided to move from Colorado to the hippie haven of Deadwood, Oregon, where Stardust became a sales rep for Little Debbie Frosted Fudge Cakes and Yardley took a position as manager of the faux foods division of the Oregon Cattlemen's Association.

Preparing for the new Congress, Holly Hawkins, Charlie Harrison, and Randy Lesher sent newsletters to their member companies, touting their appointment to the National Cricket Commission's blue-ribbon panel. Although the commission had absolutely nothing to do with what their members cared about, they spun it as a high honor and further proof of the insider role they played in the development of agriculture policy. The importance of this new body could not be overstated, as evidenced by the fact that Trip Tanglewood, son of Congressman Mark Tanglewood, had agreed to give up his high-powered logistics position to take the reins of this new organization. Their involvement with this highly touted blue-ribbon board would make them a critical component in the creation of farm policy for years to come.

While the DC merry-go-round was underway, P. J. "Snakeboots" Jackson was back to doing what he did best, recruiting new clients for the 119th Congress. He had already signed the National Cricket Commission to a six-figure retainer to act as outside general counsel. He also had been hired by NASA to investigate how bread-like crumbs had contaminated the air vent system of the space shuttle, requiring the agency to abort their latest mission. In addition, the newly created Swine Institute at the Department of Agriculture had been in contact regarding a one-year contract for him to provide professional advice and guidance as needed.

Things were looking up for Snakeboots as he had lunch under his picture at the Palm with a potential new client—the Petroleum Institute Clean Air Coalition. Already three members of Congress had stopped by the table and offered to help in any way they could.

Some things never change.

ABOUT GEORGE FRANKLIN

As a lawyer, lobbyist, and former Vice President of Worldwide Government Affairs for Kellogg Company, George has an insider's perspective on how Washington works and doesn't. He spent years in the halls of Congress as a major player on behalf of the food industry where he developed the anecdotes and saw firsthand the outrageous personalities parodied in his books.

GeorgeFranklinAuthor.com
 @georgefranklinauthor